The Sky is Falling...
So They Called Me!
Vol. 1

PatientExperiencePress
3600 Harwood Road
Suite A
Bedford, TX 76021
www.PatientExperiencePress.org

ISBN 978-0-9903728-0-6
Printed in the United States of America

Barbara Mahlbrorche

Forward

Year after year members of the Society for Healthcare Consumer Advocacy (SHCA) Board of Directors work hard to improve, enhance, and promote the field of patient advocacy. As a new board member in 2003, I was amazed at the tremendous focus the Board had as our President and my professional mentor, Lisa Reynolds, led the Society through a very successful year. During that year my eyes were opened to the multifaceted issues the board faced and the work they accomplished.

For me, one of the best benefits of being a SHCA member is being able to gather together with other professionals in the advocacy field and share stories. Patient advocates come from countless environments – hospitals that can be large, rural, urban, small, specialty, Veteran's Administration or other; or specialty clinics, Canadian healthcare organizations, inner city facilities or, perhaps, teaching hospitals, to name just a few, and each of us has stories to share.

In 2004, under the leadership of President Brenda Radford, SHCA's Board faced new issues and took on the huge task of challenging new grievance standards from the Centers for Medicare and Medicaid Services. Once again we told stories about our work experiences to balance the work at hand with CMS and other important business. From funny tales to serious stories, we recognized the incredible "story" that patient advocates across the US and Canada had to tell. So, the idea of ***The Sk y is Falling So They Called Me*** was born.

2005 brought SHCA under the leadership of President, Irene Zbiczak, and another year of hard work and great times with friends. In 2006 Board member Tammy Miller put her heart and soul into making the idea of this publication to reality.

On behalf of SHCA members and patient advocates everywhere, who are passionate to make the healthcare experience better, who take their jobs seriously, and who believe in being a voice for patients, I hope you enjoy reading these stories, and that they give you a glimpse into the lives and hearts of patient advocacy.

Mary Barks 2006
President
Society for Healthcare Consumer Advocacy

Countless thanks to all of the contributors to this book who generously shared their stories of Consumer Advocates:

Alice Rothermel	Malinda Rutledge-Carlisle
Ann Leiss	Manny Acosta
Barbara Cameron	Marlene Gallo
Bonnie G. Wheeler, PRC	Marlene R. Dees
Brenda Radford	Martica Pitt
Carolyn Stiefel	Mary Lou Novak, R.N.
Cathy Marketto	Mary Lou Stinson LPN
Cheryl Deemer	Mary Washington Hospital
Christine Brown	Melissa Carowick
Claire Gerstein	Michele L. Long
Cris Danielson	Pam Mann
Dana Ramey	Pamela K. Parker
Debra Wills	Pat Evans
Ellen Morrison RN, BC	Patricia F. Freeman
Ellen Tobert	Renee Salzbrenner
Gail Stanley	Robyn Schenning, R.N.
Harrison Silverdale	Rosalie K. Dwyer
Jacquelyn Sue Lydic	Rosalie Mercein Sullivan
Janet E. Wiseman	Ruth Sullivan
Janet Pakish	Savena Stemper
Jennifer Dicks	Sue Scardina
Judy Henry	Tammy Miller
Judy Moon McGaha	Theresa Randall
Kristi Strange	Thom L. Juarros
Laura Saltzman-Trazzi, LCSW-C	Tita E. Roach RN BSN
Laura Trazzi, LCSW-C	Victoria Hart
Linda McLean	Virginia Potrepka, RN
Linda Tyre	Wanda Llewellyn
Lisa Reynolds	Wendy Atkinson
Louise Macaulay	

Finally, we extend our very special thanks to the co-editors of this publication, Janet Pakish and Bonnie Wheeler, as they provided a wealth of knowledge and wisdom. We express our sincere gratitude for their contributions to this very special project.

Index of Stories

98 and Sharper Than You and Me Put Together

As the sole patient rep in a busy ER, I quickly learned that the way to cover my off hours was to train volunteers to work in the ER. Most of the volunteers were eager pre-med students from local colleges, so I was surprised when an ER doc suggested a slightly older candidate.

I was at home, on a day off, when the phone rang. "This is Dr. Johnson, and I have a fantastic volunteer for you!" Dr. Johnson wasn't one of my bigger supporters, so I thought he must be really bored and playing a prank on me. I explained that it was really great that he was recruiting volunteers, but could he please have the potential volunteer call me next week to set up an appointment? "No, no... You don't understand! This guy is fantastic!!! He's 98 years old and he needs something to do! He'd be GREAT in the ER!!!"

Now I KNEW this was a joke. "Dr. Johnson, I'm hanging up the phone now. I know you're bored, but this is a little extreme." Dr. Johnson stubbornly refused to let me get back to enjoying my weekend. "No, wait! Really, this guy is fantastic. He's 98 and he's sharper than you and I put together. Will you please call him next week and get him in here?"

Am I ever glad that I listened to Dr. Johnson! I called the 98- year-old gentleman the next week, and our hospital embarked on what would become a wonderful relationship with this amazing volunteer for the next four years. While he didn't work in the ER, he provided phenomenal support to many patients in our skilled nursing center. And, he was sharper than Dr. Johnson and a few others, plus me put together.

A Basket of Candy

Eleanor was a diabetic patient who was a "frequent flyer" at the medical center. She was visited by Mary, the patient advocate, who asked, as she was leaving, "Is there anything I can do for you before I leave?" Eleanor jokingly replied, "You can get me some candy."

Mary stopped to check with the nurse, then went to the gift shop and bought Eleanor a bag of sugar free candy. What a surprise when Mary delivered the candy!

A few weeks later, Eleanor was back in the hospital. When Linda, the patient advocate volunteer, visited her, Eleanor mentioned how Mary had bought her some sugar free candy from the gift shop. However, when Linda visited the gift shop, all of the sugar free candy was sold out. Linda went to the nearest grocery store, bought a wicker basket and filled it with every kind of sugar free candy the store carried. Eleanor could not b e li e v e her eyes when the basket was delivered to her. She was so delighted!

We expected this to be an ongoing saga of finding sugar free candy for Eleanor, but she unexpectedly died during the week after she was discharged back to the nursing home. Mary and Linda were so thankful they had taken the time to make this small difference in Eleanor's life.

A Father's Dying Wish

I had an occasion to work with a family that brought both satisfaction and frustration, and also helped me appreciate the freedom and opportunities we have here in the United States.

A man was admitted into our hospital with a diagnosis of lung cancer. Although now a US citizen, he was originally from Pakistan and three of his children still lived there. He had begun the process of trying to bring his two younger children, age 17 & 18, to the U.S. under the Immigration Program. He had the papers partially completed for sponsorship, the final stage, when he received his diagnosis.

Time became of the essence as the doctor had told him his cancer was very advanced and was already spreading throughout his body. His eldest son was living in Belgium and the patient asked my assistance in trying to contact him to come to the U.S. This was not difficult to accomplish: a few phone calls and faxes to the American Embassy in Belgium helped secure his son a visa and three days later he was at his father's bedside. It was amazing to see the instant change in the father as soon as his son arrived. No medicine in the world could have brought about this change!

However, the challenge of trying to bring his two children from Pakistan was another story! I started with faxes to the American Embassy in Pakistan together with phone calls to the family. The embassy consistently denied receiving the faxes. I was sure they were going through; as the family was receiving the faxes I sent them! Eventually out of frustration I turned to the local office of our congressman for help.

The young lady I spoke with had attended a workshop on precisely this matter the previous week – trying to help people dealing with immigration problems. Was this fate or what! She was extremely helpful and made all kinds of calls and sent faxes. She really went out of her way to help. It was not easy making contact and because of the ten-hour time difference we had to do everything in the late evening to coincide with the workday in Pakistan.

Things looked quite hopeful and the father, despite his obviously serious condition, was able to muster a smile at the thought of seeing his children again before he died. But as the days went by, hope seemed to fade. The embassy kept stalling and wanting additional information, and it soon became apparent that they were not going to grant even visitor's visas to the children. The father seemed to understand that his youngest children would not be coming to the United States, and two days later he died with his eldest son at his bedside.

I was grateful I had at least been able to reunite father and son, but it was very sad to think that his younger children were denied the opportunity of saying goodbye to their family because of bureaucratic red tape! I thank God every day for the blessings He bestows upon us, and the freedom – Oh the freedom!

A Flight to Remember

Ten-year-old Hope had been a patient in this pediatric department for years, suffering from chronic kidney and cardiac conditions. She had been a frequent inpatient, and she and her family had become very comfortable with the pediatric patient representative.

One evening around 9:00, the Patient Representative received a phone call at home from Hope's mother. Hope had been experiencing chest pain and had been trying to contact the Pediatric Cardiac resident on call for about thirty minutes, but hadn't been able to reach him.

Hope's mom was getting ready to take her to the local hospital (since she lived about two and a half hours away from the major medical center that she frequented). However, she really felt that it was important to speak with her physician or a member of the team. She was frantic and asked if the patient representative could try to contact the resident, since no one would answer her call.

The patient rep was glad to do this and learned that something had happened when one resident was switched on-call responsibilities to another resident. The resident-on-call was not actually getting the page.

The patient rep proceeded to page the attending physician, who called back quickly. He was quite concerned with Hope's symptoms and, even though he was in the grocery store, contacted her local physician immediately. Arrangements were made for Hope to be transported via "Life Flight" to our hospital.

When the helicopter arrived at their local hospital, Mom learned that she would not be able to travel with Hope to our hospital; she was very upset. Hope had never been left alone with any healthcare provider in her entire life, and Mom was not thrilled about her being in the helicopter alone. She was especially concerned about Hope arriving at the Emergency Room alone.

The patient representative's phone rang again just before midnight. Once again it was Hope's mother, crying and very scared. The patient rep assured the mother that Hope would be well cared for on the helicopter, and added that if it would make her feel more comfortable, she, herself, would meet Hope at the helicopter pad and remain with her until her mother arrived.

As promised, the patient representative went back to the hospital at 1:00 AM to meet the child. Since this was the first time that Hope had ever ridden in a helicopter, she was having a grand time but, all the same, was very happy to see a familiar face when she arrived at the Emergency Room, and relieved to have someone stay by her side until her parents arrived.

To this day, Hope and her mother tell everyone they know about this story, making the patient representative feels like she is part of their family.

A Mother's Words

Patient representatives most often deal with conflict and dissatisfaction. Occasionally, though, "when the sky is falling" it can be a positive experience for the family.

Mary, age 79, had died at our hospital recently. The day after her death I received a phone call from the daughter, who said, "If Mom could talk with the doctors and nurses, she would say: "Thank you for the incredible, compassionate care you've given me. You could give the class on death and dying because you have a special way with people. The staff caring was exceptionally wonderful, including the harp and soft CD music, which I loved, to the hospitality cart for my family. You have the right thing going."

The daughter further stated that Mary was a person who appreciated the goodness in everyone, often complimenting the city street worker for doing a fine job. She told the patient representative "We are done with the tears already, because Mom deserved special care and she received it".

The remainder of my day was filled with more dissatisfaction; however, nothing could change the beauty of that day in my life as a patient representative.

A Son's Wish

Drew Horton, a 21-year-old patient, has been in our hospital for the past two months. Prognosis is not favorable, and it does not appear he will survive his cancer diagnosis.
Drew learned our hospital provides a licensed cosmetologist who is available to come to patients' rooms to give haircuts and manicures. However, Drew is bald as a result of his chemotherapy and the clinical nurse specialist was confused as to why he was interested in the services.

Drew indicated he wanted the services for his mother who has been his loving support and has stayed with him during his long hospital stay. He was extremely disappointed when we had to relay to him that unfortunately the cosmetologist could only perform services for patients – not for family members or visitors.

It was with heartfelt pleasure that with the assistance of the clinical nurse specialist and our department, guest services, we arranged to have the beauty salon located across from our hospital, donate a fifty dollar gift certificate to Drew's mother so we could fulfill Drew's wish – a loving gift to his mother from a loving, caring son.

A Suitcase?

The day is not complete for many advocates until they have heard the threat, "I'm going to file a suit."

I knew I had heard it all one day when my peer, the facility's risk manager, had a call from a young woman who had experienced a 30-minute wait in the ED with her infected toe. She stated that she was filing a "suitcase" against the facility for the wait.

Less than two hours later, another young patient called to say she had a 45-minute wait to be seen for her sinus headache, and that she was filing a "suitcase."

The risk manager and I laughed. We obviously had a matching set of "luggage."

A True Hero

It was just another day for guest service specialist, Daniel Hawkins, when the call came.

The driver of an 18-wheeler, who had been delivering materials nearby, had to be rushed to LMC because of a possible heart attack. As the driver was being admitted, he expressed concern for his dog Susie who was in the truck's cab at the delivery site. "My dad works at the site, and I know my way around there, so I drove over immediately," recalls Daniel. "Susie was sitting in the cab, very scared, and when she saw me her ears popped up in the air. With a lot of coaxing she finally let me pick her up and put her in my car."

The real problem came when Daniel got to the vet's office that had offered to house Susie until her owner was better. It had taken Daniel so long to calm the shaken Susie that the office had closed for the evening. So without a moment's hesitation, Daniel took little Susie home, where she slept all night next to his bed.

"I don't consider what I did that incredible," says Daniel. "I just thought about how important my own dog is to me. Our job in guest services is to take care of patients, and that includes their families. I consider dogs a part of the family."

For his willingness to go above and beyond, Daniel Hawkins received LMC's Hero Award. We are proud to call him a member of the LMC family.

A Warm, Friendly, Familiar Face

My grandfather was recently hospitalized approximately 30 miles from my home and was not expected to live. Even though my grandfather lived a long, happy life, 87 years, you are never fully prepared for all the end-of-life issues that present themselves. I remember my grandfather being a strong, proud man with big muscles he earned while working for many years as a laborer with the railroad.

In his hospital bed, he was a shell of the man he used to be. Cancer had consumed his body and was slowly, but surely, shutting down every organ. When the hospital's patient care representative entered the room, she was like a breath of fresh air. I recognized her warm, friendly, familiar face because she was a fellow state society member. I always felt she lit up a room when she entered. She genuinely cares for those she serves.

Her visit meant a great deal to my family and made us realize we were not in this alone. She and the entire hospital staff were there for us every step of the way and made sure we, as well as my grandfather, were comfortable. As my grandfather slipped away and took his final breath, the majority of the staff who had cared for him wept openly with the family.

This reinforced what I already knew: as healthcare professionals, what we do for our patients and their family makes a huge difference and impacts their lives.

A Wedding Planner

The week had been overwhelming. Patients, families and problems had been constant and left me counting the minutes until I could leave the office that Friday afternoon. I was praying for a quiet, refreshing weekend to regenerate my weary bones and being.

While tying up loose ends at my desk, the site director of nursing flew around the corner into my office. He wanted me to know that there was a family in the ED with an unusual situation. A fifty-year-old male was brought in by ambulance with advanced cancer. Accompanying him was his devoted, who tearfully said that their family had planned a 19th wedding anniversary party for them the following day. This was especially important since they knew that he would never live to see their 20th anniversary.

Family and friends were already on their way from out of town. The party was to be held at a local church. The site director asked if we could possibly do something to accommodate this family, since we knew the gentleman would still be an inpatient the next day.

The education director, site director and I sprang into action. We showed the wife our humble conference rooms, hoping she would realize they were in the process of being remodeled. She became even more tearful when we offered to "host" their anniversary party right there in the hospital. She and the family could not believe that we were so willing to assist them in making sure that the party would still take place.

Working late into the evening, we worked our magic. Tables were set and decorated, a borrowed ficus tree and a set of twinkling white Christmas lights borrowed from someone's office helped transform the drab meeting rooms into a sparkling setting ready to celebrate this joyous occasion the following day.

I was up and at the hospital early the morning of the ceremony. On our makeshift altar I placed a spectacular bouquet of pink roses – a gift from the hospital. Pink and white balloons greeted the guests at the front door and led them to the event location.

Luscious smells from food prepared with great love wafted from the room.

Meanwhile word of the event rippled throughout the hospital. Staff used every excuse imagined to come to the first floor to peak into the rooms to get a glimpse of the preparations. The air was filled with excitement.

The patient's lab reports were not good. As a matter of fact, almost anyone else who was that ill would have been non- responsive, but not this man. Not only was he alert – he was so excited the staff could hardly contain him! Plans had been made to wheel him to the conference rooms to preserve his energy.
The "groom" would not hear of that and insisted on walking the long hallway unassisted.

While he stood at the altar the music began to play and in walked his beautiful "bride." She wore a long white gown and could not take her eyes off her handsome groom as she walked the aisle towards him. They had each written vows to each other and together they asked God to give them additional time to be together in this life. Staff filled the back of the room and there was not a dry eye to be found. Food, fun and wonderful memories filled the afternoon. The couple even celebrated with a dance and wedding cake, homemade and beautifully decorated by their daughter.

Later in the day when the last guest left and the last of the clean up was finished, I reflected on what a joy the day had been. In a profession that sees so much sadness, what a privilege it was to share in something so meaningful to a family. Nearly every guest repeatedly expressed sincere thanks for our willingness to see a need and do what needed to be done to see that this family could celebrate such a great occasion.

By the way, did you know that an overhead projector stand makes a great cake table?

Absentee Voting

The 2004 presidential election was fraught with emotion. Opinions ran deep, resulting in record voter turnout across the nation. Our county was no different.

One little lady in the cardiac care unit was very upset; she had been brought to the hospital and would not be able to vote. She complained to a friend, who called the patient relations office about her dilemma. After listening to this patient's story, we contacted our local elections office to see if we could help her, and other patients, make their vote count.

The staff at our facility got behind the effort. Within 48 hours, our marketing department had designed and produced tent cards to go on all the breakfast trays, letting the patients know to contact the patient relations office to obtain assistance in voting. Nursing staff helped get the word out to those patients who did not get breakfast.

The elections office provided us with applications for absentee ballots, which we hand-delivered to all patients who requested assistance in voting. We then took the completed applications to the elections office, and they checked their computers and provided the appropriate ballots. Absentee ballots were delivered to the patients in their hospital rooms, and the completed ballots were delivered to the polls on Election Day.

The 2004 state general election hit the national news as one of the closest elections in history. Votes were counted, re- recounted, and counted again. In the end, the new governor was elected by a handful of votes.

Our little lady in the CCU was ecstatic that she had been able to vote. Thanks to her friend's call, 23 other patients were able to vote, as well. But, the nicest outcome of the entire project was that, for two days, we put aside our partisanship, ignored the mudslinging, and worked together to exercise our right to vote.

An Angel's Prayer

I was called to the Emergency Department for a code blue situation. As I hurried into the trauma area, I saw the wife of a patient, a lady in her 70's, married over fifty years. She was accompanied by a sister with whom she had just been reunited, and a nephew.

She was terribly shaken, and was waiting for information about her husband's condition, although he had been very sick for a long time. After speaking with a nurse about the situation, I went to help the family find and call other family members, as they knew the patient was not doing well.

Before and after talking with the family, I stopped inconspicuously to say prayer for them. During that time the doctor and nurses were in and out of the patient's room; the wife had spoken with her husband while he was still conscience, but after a time, there was nothing more to do other than wait.

The family mentioned "God's Will" a couple times and noted the wishes of the patient. They were a quiet family who spoke lovingly to each other. I noticed the sister glancing toward me occasionally then looking away; she seemed to be gazing just above my head. She had a strange look on her face each time this happened but seemed content.

After a while the physician came in to let the wife know that they had done everything possible to save her husband but that he had passed away. Her sister comforted her, saying that everything was going to be okay, that an angel had been with them praying the entire time, and that her husband was with the Lord. Her sister smiled sweetly in response, thanked me and continued to hold her sister.

Baby Timmy

We all travel different paths to our jobs as patient reps.

My husband and I parented six children (homemade, adopted and long-term foster) who all had various disabilities; as a result I spent most of my early parenting years as an advocate for my own children. In my late 40's I had the great fortune to be blessed with a job as a patient rep – a blending of past experience and new challenges.

Baby Timmy was born with a rare syndrome that caused extensive deformities in his little limbs. Whenever Timmy's mother took him out in public she would wrap him tightly (even though it was summer) so that no one could see his arms or legs.

Timmy's parents were so paralyzed and dysfunctional since his birth that the staff had serious concerns about their ability to care for him. Timmy's condition required frequent casting of his little legs. The orthopedic nurse knew about my background and thought that perhaps I could help. With the doctor's approval, I was given a clear description of what to expect when I saw Timmy.

I swept into the casting room where I saw the tiny infant laying half naked on the exam table. The doctor and nurse tried to introduce me to the parents as Timmy screamed at the top of his very healthy lungs. Timmy was hungry, the doctor was frustrated, and the parents huddled helplessly in a corner of the room.

It was love at first sight for me. I scooped up the screaming infant, rhapsodizing about his beautiful red curls and his winsome face. The doctor waited patiently while I cuddled, cooed, calmed and fed the baby. When he finally started casting those tiny misshapen legs I just continued loving Timmy, while starting to talk to his parents. I was oblivious to anything but the sight of a beautiful baby boy.

Mom and I exchanged stories and phone numbers. I gave her a copy of a parent's book I had authored (she eventually wore out several copies). It was with sincere reluctance that I handed the now-casted baby over to his mother.

The ortho staff said that they noticed a transformation during the next visit. Mom and Dad soothed their son while his casts were changed, and he was wearing a cute summer romper that exposed his arms and legs. Mom enthused to the nurse about a slight improvement in Timmy that she had noticed. The staff said that the change started the moment I came into the room on the previous visit and fell in love with Timmy - not noticing any deformities – just seeing his beauty and loving him (something I'd been doing with my own children for years.) Timmy's casts were changed weekly and his parents and I had many opportunities to visit.

My original patient relations goal had been to use my experiences to help others. My experience with Timmy and his family was one of those awesome occasions of serendipity where past and present intersect.

By the way, the last time I heard from Timmy's mother it seems he's turned out to be a computer whiz!

Bea: A Story About Assumptions

This is a hard story to tell since it involves revealing a fault of mine early in my career at the hospital. Here it goes anyway…

We had a patient by the name of Bea. She would come into the hospital all the time especially around the holidays. Most of us felt she was lonely and wanted to be around other people since her husband was dead. Every time Bea would come in, I would visit w i t h her to discuss her discharge plans. Each time she would tell me that her wonderful son and his loving wife would take care of her. However, I never saw her son or daughter-in-law the numerous times she would come in. I thought Bea was just saying this to appease the doctor and me. I began to grow very fond of Bea; she reminded me of my own grandmother. I often wondered if she s p e n t lonely days at home with no visitors. I was always worried about how Bea would get along, not really believing she had family who cared. They would have visited if they did care, right? Then death took Bea. I went to her funeral and finally met the son she had always talked about. He was very nice and I told him of how special his mother was to me. He ended up comforting me. I then felt that Bea was right and truly was blessed with a loving and caring son.

Several years later when my children played high school sports, I re-met Bea's son. He and his wife attend all the high school sports activities in our town. I have personally witnessed the care and affection he gives to his ailing wife. He devotedly gets her out of their vehicle and in a wheelchair, gets her snacks and dotingly sits by her side during the events. He is his wife's complete caregiver. Now I know how much Bea's son had played an important role in Bea's life. Thanks to him, she was able to avoid going to a nursing home and spent her last days at home where she wanted to be.

I learned a valuable lesson from him. Just because I could not feel or touch Bea's son's presence here at the hospital, does not mean he did not care. I have grown to respect this man for what he does and the love he exudes when I see him care for his wife. I know that one has to look inside the book to get the meaning, not the cover.

Be Careful Who You Advocate For

One thing that is very neat about establishing relationships with fellow patient advocates from other area hospitals is that you have someone to call when you are transferring a patient to a nearby facility. Our hospital receives many referrals from a hospital that is two hours south of us. Unfortunately many accidents happen in that town, which has a major highway busy with people traveling back and forth from north to south.

On this particular day, our patient rep office received a call from the referring facility's department director about an accident. The patient was being transferred via life light to our hospital.

The patient's car had been totaled in the accident, and the patient's brother who was traveling with him, had no funds for transportation to our facility. A local church offered to purchase the gentleman a bus ticket; the referring facility was wondering if we could make arrangements to pick him up at the bus station and help him find a place for the night. Of course we were happy to do this. With the information about the name of the patient and his brother, we made arrangements transportation and a complimentary room in a hotel across the street from the hospital.

The following morning I contacted the hotel to update the visitor on his brother's status, and to let him know that we had meal passes available for his use in our hospital cafeteria. After several unsuccessful attempts to reach him, I called the hotel manager who went to the room to wake him.

The gentleman finally called me, and we arranged to meet in the hospital lobby. I found it unusual that he was much more interested in eating than checking on his brother, but I gave him meal passes for the day. Then I told him how to get up to see his brother, who was just back to his room after surgery.

When I checked in on the patient, I let him know his brother was in the cafeteria. He didn't seem too concerned with seeing his brother, but I assured him that his he would be visited soon.

At this point my instincts were telling me that something was wrong with this situation, so I paid a call on the hospital's chief of police. After being provided with the names of the patient and his brother, which were not the same, the chief ran a check on both of them.

Lo and behold, he found that the "brother" was wanted in several counties for drug charges. The police chief met with the patient and found out that the accident had actually occurred because of a drug deal gone bad. The man in the cafeteria was in no way related to the patient, and I had been unknowingly aiding and abetting a criminal!

In the end, both men were arrested and, thank God, the police chief knew me well, or I guess I would have been in cuffs as well.

Sometimes it pays to be sure you know for whom you are advocating!!!

Blankets of Love

One morning about two months ago, I received a call from our nursing staff requesting a "Blanket of Love" for a patient on our Oncology unit, who was dying. Blankets of Love are made, or donated, by our hospital staff and friends who volunteer their time to this project. The Blankets of Love are given to special patients as a token of our caring, and as a shared memory of the special place they hold in our hearts.

We attach a card to the quilt that reads:

"May you be warmed by a Blanket of Love".
There are no more special people to us than those who allow us to care for them. In the time we spend together, bonds are formed and shared memories are built. Each one holds a special place in our hearts.
We would like to share with you this Blanket of Love, stitched by a volunteer who knew it would go to a very special person. We hope it will wrap you in love and warm your heart as you have warmed ours.

When I was able to secure a blanket the following morning, the staff informed me that this patient had expired, but her 23-year- old daughter was now a patient. She also was fighting serious cancer; was an employee of ours and had a three-year-old daughter. She shared that her mother's favorite color had been purple; so I secured a large purple blanket in memory of her mother; and a small one for her daughter (the granddaughter). One of the most feminine, lovely blankets I could find, I presented to the daughter.

We all hope she beats her battle. She continues to be a patient now and then, as she continues with her treatments.

Boo!

I am one of four patient advocates for the Volunteers Hospitals in Texas and my story takes place in the Emergency Department.

One night linens were running low in the Emergency Room. Because all of the nurses were working with patients, and were unable to replace the linens, I volunteered to go for a supply from the linen room, located in the hospital's basement.

The basement can be a scary place late in the evening, with its curvy hallways shaped like a maze; not to mention the morgue appealingly located there…. The hallway set up is so confusing that you actually think about leaving a trail of breadcrumbs to find the way back out again.

After traversing successfully to the linen room, I found the door was locked, so I went the environmental office nearby. I asked a staff person in that office if she could she open the linens door for me. While she called the supervisor, I waited patiently in the hallway.

I could hear voices. They grew louder. Suddenly a young man came out of environmental services. Turning around he caught a glimpse of me standing there; his face was horrified. I looked back at him and in a quiet voice said, "Boo!" I scared him so badly he ran over and hugged me tight!

I know he really wanted to ring my neck, but a hug was much better for both of us. Every time after that we pass in the hall we both remember that night and share a little giggle. The things we advocates do for outpatients!

Now, don't go anywhere because my story gets better. The day came when I got my "pay back" for scaring that young man so badly.

While working in the Emergency Department another evening, I was talking with a patient and their family. Preparing to exit the room, I grabbed the privacy curtain to pull it back. My hand encountered another hand on the opposite side of the drape. You can't imagine the fright that went through me in that moment. Pulling myself together, I pulled the curtain back to find…a nurse standing there.

I asked the nurse if he knew I was coming out; he hadn't. As I was catching my breath, I said, "Well you certainly scared me, did I scare you?" Of course his reply was no. I then recalled the time I was waiting in a hallway and scared a young coworker.

We patient advocates take extra steps for our patient's every day. While loving our careers, once in a while a situation arises that gives us something to giggle about. Spreading laughter is very contagious and it takes away the pain for at least a couple of seconds; well at least it did that night for my patient and their family.

Charlie and Penny's Wedding: Intensive Caring

On Monday morning at 10 a.m. my e-mail message read, "Charlie, a patient in ICU, is getting married today. Could you arrange for the bride to have flowers and possibly a cake?" I went to the unit where I found the bridal couple.

Charlie was receiving blood, had several IV's running and was on continuous oxygen. He was a large man and appeared to be very ill. Penny, his bride to be, was right there by his side. She was a petite lady, who proudly announced that she was 74. She told me she and her intended had accepted the Lord on Saturday and wanted to get married in the sight of God and the world.

I questioned Penny about her favorite colors and began making arrangements for the bridal bouquet and cake. Then I called the newspaper, a photographer, and a soloist. I wanted this to be a memorable day for Charlie and Penny.

Later in the afternoon, friends of the couple brought in a white lace bridal gown and helped Penny with her hair and makeup. They also arranged for a pastor to come in to perform the ceremony. Shortly before 4 p.m., the newspaper reporter arrived and talked with the groom to get some background information. The photographer arrived and began shooting candid shots while waiting for the bride.

Charlie, who was a World II veteran said, "I want Penny to get my pension from the government when I'm gone because I need to make sure she's cared for." While showing the reporter his medicine man clothes, Charlie told him that he met Penny because they were both descended from the Cherokee Indian Nation. He shared with pride some of the history behind his necklace and the one he had for Penny to wear during the ceremony.

While nurses, lab techs, respiratory therapists, physicians, and other hospital staff and friends gathered, the beaming couple exchanged their vows. Just as they said their "I do's," an administrative assistant arrived to sing, "Oh Perfect Love." Everyone ate cake and toasted the newly married couple.

Later that evening, Charlie's breathing became increasingly difficult, and by dawn he was near death. His sons arrived from out of state and joined Penny at his bedside during his last hours. He passed away the next afternoon with a look of peace and contentment on his face, with his new bride holding his hand.

Christmas Stamps

The holiday rush was on and along with that came increased census and patients who had needs above and beyond medications and treatments...the mailing of their Christmas cards.

I had been summoned early in the morning to a nursing unit to see an elderly lady who had been working on her Christmas cards for several days. She always mailed them early and being in the hospital was not going to prevent that from happening this year. Her request of me was to obtain postage stamps – 200 of them.

I assured her that before I left work that day I would purchase the stamps from our gift shop and return to her with stamps in hand.

The best plans of patient advocate quickly go astray. My pager continued to require my attention to a multitude of other patient and family issues during the morning.

Over the lunch hour I rushed into the gift shop and obtained two sheets of 100 stamps and added them to the collection of items in my already full arms. I quickly reviewed in my mind the afternoon agenda and decided to stop at my office to drop some things off and pick up other items needed for my afternoon meetings.

As is also the case with patient advocate's when we get to our offices the phone is ringing and we cannot let a ringing phone rest. So answer it I did.

The phone call required I sit down and take notes regarding the care and treatment the caller had not received from our staff during a recent hospitalization.

Following the phone conversation I collected my necessary items for the afternoon and took off out the door. I returned to my office about 3:00 pm and realized I needed to deliver the stamps.

I picked up the papers I had with me when I purchased the stamps, expecting to find the stamps with them. I couldn't find them anywhere, so I called the gift shop thinking I may have left them on the counter after paying for them. I soon learned that was not the case.

I retraced my steps from the afternoon to the various areas and rooms that I had been in and, as my luck would have it, there were a lot of places, people and things. But the stamps were not to be found; until, that is, I walked by a group of people waiting for an elevator.

I paused to visit with a staff member when I felt a gentle tap on my shoulder. A soft voice whispered in my ear, "Are you aware you have several pages of stamps attached to your backside?"

"Oh no," I replied, only to place my hand firmly behind me. It wasn't a Christmas miracle, but truly the missing stamps had been found.

I hurried to the patient's room to deliver her much-needed postage for her Christmas cards. I told her the stamps already had a few miles on them having traveled with me throughout the hospital - I just didn't mention the method mode of transportation.

Christy

Christy was an intelligent, well-spoken lady. She had leukemia, but it was in remission. She was admitted to the medical center for an elective, routine surgery and was very optimistic. She was also an outspoken believer in advance directives and made it clear that she had her living will declaration completed and had a medical power of attorney. In the event of a problem, she did not want resuscitation. She had even plans made to go into hospice if her leukemia returned.

I visited her for routine advance directive follow-up. As her few family members did not live near-by, I told her I would visit as frequently as possible. I wished her well with her surgery and told her I would see her soon.

The next day I went to her room and found she was in a coma and had been transferred to critical care. She was on a respirator, not responsive, and heavily sedated. Knowing of her advance directives I spoke with her doctor. He said her condition was not terminal and not connected to her leukemia, and he felt she would pull through.

I kept my promise and visited her nearly every day. She did not respond to me or know I was there, but I felt compelled just to tell her I was there and to assure her that she would be all right.

A week passed. Now the need to advocate for her wishes was of growing concern. The doctor maintained his belief that she would pull through, and was talking with her niece, to whom Christy had appointed power of attorney. The young niece did not know what to do, but had faith in the doctor.

Another week passed and the patient was still in a coma, her condition unchanged. Christy's niece called to say she would be coming to town and wanted advice. I arranged for her to meet with the chaplain, the physician and me.

The doctor met with her first. Her aunt had been in a coma for nearly three weeks. The physician told her he still believed Christy would pull through. He said he had treated patients in worse condition that had recovered.

The niece then met with the chaplain and me. Tearfully, she said that the responsibility for deciding was too hard, she wanted to give her aunt every chance, but she knew that being sustained on life support was not Christy's wish. When, she asked, would she know that enough was enough? It had been three weeks and her aunt was not responding. The Chaplain told her she would know. He said, "Your heart will tell you. Have faith and the answer will come."

The next day the doctor began to wean Christy from the respirator. Two days later Christy opened her eyes. Three days later she was responding and could tell when someone was near; her recovery had begun.

Told she probably would not walk again and that she might not remember all that she had done before, she decided that God was not yet ready for her and that there were things she was supposed to accomplish. Wrapped in this faith, she doggedly kept trying to get better.

Sometimes when I visited, she would be practicing her handwriting in crayon: at first it looked like a young child learning to print her name. It gradually got better and she went to a pencil and started to remember how to write in script. Christy began PT, trying to gain strength in her legs. Always optimistic, our "miracle patient" was determined to get on with the work she wanted to finish, like writing her book and returning to work with the children in her church. After many weeks, she was ready for discharge and chose to go to a care facility near her niece.

Some months later I received a card from Christy. Her cursive handwriting (in pen!) was better than mine and she had begun to walk using a walker. She looked forward to her new life, never regretting the decisions that had been made on her behalf.

Christy reminded us of the power of faith: her faith in her niece to make the right decisions, her niece's faith in the doctor, the doctor's belief that for some reason she would pull through, her faith in herself that she could get better and her faith in her religious beliefs. I hear that Christy continues to do well and has gotten back to writing her book.

Compassion

For the past few months, Jim has worked at the Front Desk as our Guest Services Specialist and serves many people in different capacities. If I could find one word to describe his dedication it would be - compassionate.

Jim has several patients including one gentleman who has allowed Jim to become his confidante. Of course with HIPPA, we are so careful not to exchange or disclose information regarding patients but in this instance, Jim has become this patient's support network.

Our patient is currently enrolled in the cardio-pulmonary rehab and is trying to attend as many sessions as his health will allow. Unfortunately his outlook is poor but he remains steadfast in trying to come because he knows that "that is what is keeping me alive".

Our patient has informed me that, "Jim is an angel: he listens, advises, and even calls me at home to check on me when I don't make it for treatments." He also says that Jim is his family and, "Without his encouragement I probably would not be here." Jim was so concerned about our patient that he visited him at home the Saturday after Thanksgiving to check on him.

This visit proved to be a lifesaving one. Jim encouraged our patient to seek further treatment because of the patient's condition change. Through a series of doctor visits, he is now hospitalized in our ICU and remarkably is better.

At this writing, Jim continues to check-on our patient, quietly giving me updates as to what is happening with his new extended family. I know that we have many heroes in our hospital but this represents taking the time to really care and certainly goes beyond what is expected. I believe that we could use this as an example of the New Haven Medical Center's giving spirit!

Cookie Monster

While attempting to type patient letters to meet CMS guidelines, the phone rang displaying the Administration number on my caller ID. I immediately knew a patient with a complaint would be transferred to me or I would be asked to meet with a patient; but what was soon to transpire, I never could have imagined.

The Administrative Secretary asked me to meet her because something had just "dropped" in her lap that she was unsure how to handle. As I arrived at the administration office to help, I noticed the food services manager, a jolly lady wearing a hair net and an apron was there as well. They both appeared puzzled and began to catch me up on the situation

Ms. Mom, a 79-year-old widow on our rehabilitation unit, ordered four-dozen cookies and requested they be ready for her to take home at discharge. My first thought was the patient had good taste, because I LOVE our cookies too. The food services staff was preparing them and it would be a matter of minutes before they were ready. Ms. Mom was had no problem waiting. The problem was her son had just become aware of the cookie order.

Now aware of the cookie order, Mr. Son marched to Administration demanding the order be cancelled. He told the Administrative Secretary it was negligent of us to allow his "fat" mother to order these cookies because she would sit down and eat them all in one sitting."

Mr. Son then marched back to the discharge suite to and loudly announced to the staff if Mrs. Mom was not ready for discharge in two minutes he would leave without her.

It was decided Ms. Mom was not on a restricted diet and she had paid for her order; therefore, it was her right to have the cookies. As a compromise to Ms. Mom and Mr. Son, I would take the cookies to Mr. Son at the discharge suite and explain to him that Ms. Mom was not on a restricted diet and perhaps we could find a way to make them both happy. I picked up the two trays of cookies and Ms. Mom's check (in case Mr. Son continued to refuse the order) and began to walk to the discharge suite.

As I passed, the Administrative Secretary waived me down for a phone call. It was a nurse from the discharge area telling me to call Security to accompany me to meet Mr. Son because he was threatening the staff and he was EXTREMELY angry about the cookies. I decided to leave the trays of cookies in the office, although I was tempted to eat one to prepare myself for the upcoming event. I headed towards the discharge area to speak with Mr. Son.

Being optimistic and fearless, I did not call Security. On my way, I saw a gentleman that fit Mr. Son's description; I kindly stopped him, introduced myself and asked him if he was Mr. Son. Mr. Son, at 6'2" resembled a lumberjack. He immediately pointed his finger down at me and loudly stated for everyone to hear, his mother was fat and could not have the cookies. At this point I regretted not calling security but continued to "stand tall" at 5'2". I was tempted to ask him to try a cookie and tell him that he would be hooked too, but quickly thought that he would not appreciate it. After unsuccessfully trying to calm Mr. Son, he walked down the hallway and yelled back, "If she is not down here in two minutes, I am leaving without her!"

By the time I reached the discharge suite, Ms. Mom was sitting in the passenger seat of her car and Mr. Son was loading her belongings in the trunk. As he saw me, he entered and yelled so everyone could hear him, "You all should be fired". I walked around him and approached Ms. Mom in the car. Her first response was, "Oh, you're the lady bringing me my cookies". In the best way I knew how (with all the turmoil and stares) I told Ms. Mom I did not have the cookies because her son refused to allow it and handed her the check.

Ms. Mom told me to keep the check. She began to yell at Mr. Son telling him, "He was being ridiculous." She told him prior to arriving; if he was going to act like a fool she could have had someone else pick her up. She proceeded to tell him he belonged in a "nut house" and it was her car; therefore, he was not going anywhere until the cookies were given to her. She called for the police and attempted to get out of the car because she was "not leaving without her cookies!"

The nurse and I became extremely nervous Ms. Mom might hurt herself due to her recent knee surgery. We convinced her to stay in the car by telling her we would Mail the cookies to her without her son knowing! That immediately made her happy.
She winked at me and told her son to get in the car because they were leaving without the cookies.

As soon as they drove off Security arrived to "help" the situation but stood there with nothing to do. I returned to my office to reflect on how something so simple turned into a complicated situation; and how as a team we were able to work together and in a convoluted way we made the patient happy.

Of course, the best reflections are done when eating cookies!

Cure All

Sometimes, the stories we hear from the family members of patients are stranger than the stories we hear from patients themselves. One such story came from a man who was struck by lightning.

After the strike, he began to suffer various maladies, so he sought help from a "doctor" who prescribed the perfect cure: Human breast milk taken once daily for four years. Since his wife had just given birth, he was set for the first two years.

At the end of the first two years, he had to find another source to finish his "treatment". Luckily, his neighbor had just had a baby and she was kind enough to donate to the cause until he was "cured." We were too horrified to inquire any further. Some things are better left unasked.

Denture Match

This is a game with which we are all well acquainted. A patient loses their dentures and we have the honor of finding the missing appliance.

One day I received a call that a patient had lost his dentures, so I did what every patient rep does: I spoke with the patient and got a description of the missing denture. It was a top denture having only the front four teeth. Following protocol, I contacted the linen service public safety departments, and the floor where the teeth had disappeared, stopping to speak with the staff members who cared for the patient. The dentures were nowhere to be found.

HOWEVER, a few weeks later in to my office came dentures matching the description of the lost appliance. I excitedly contacted the patient to give him the good news. He was very happy because the holidays were quickly approaching and he wanted to look his best when visiting his family.

Carefully wrapped, with the address double-checked, the dentures were sent to the patient via insured mail. Needless to say, I was very pleased with myself for helping the patient, and avoiding the hassle that comes with getting reimbursement from a state institution.

A few days later my bubble burst. A call came from the patient saying the dentures were just too small - they could not be his. I asked him to return them to me, which he did, and I began the process of arranging to have his dentures replaced. I held onto the "mystery" dentures for several months hoping to finally make a match but, alas, it wasn't meant to be.

Ah well, another day in the life of a patient representative.

Dick

Dick was a neighbor who had owned a small grocery store. When our kids visited to buy candy, he always called them by name, and greeted them at church, too. When Dick became ill a few years ago, his wife and daughter came to my office to discuss his diagnosis with me. I spoke with his physician, and then set up a meeting with the patient and family to discuss his care.

On a Saturday morning we gathered in the patient's room to have a conference. I spoke directly to Dick, "I understand from your wife that whenever you have planned a trip you have always made a list and planned your course, now you are taking your final trip and your family would like to help you with your plans." He looked at me and said, "I know what songs I want sung at my funeral...", and told me what they were.

This opened the door for the family to talk about end-of- life care issues among themselves. He wanted to go home and be in his living room so he could watch the traffic and all the action.

I followed Dick through his dying process. He and his family supported each other, and he died at home on his birthday. The songs he requested were sung at his funeral.

Later, his wife and children told me that when they started on this journey with him that they didn't know if they could handle it; but they all said it was very rewarding for them. They appreciated being able to say the things they had not said before, and hear things about their parents that they had not learned earlier.

It was rewarding for me to help the patient and his family and to give them this last gift of supporting their loved one.

Did You Want To Be an Advocate?

When you were growing up, did you say you were going to be an advocate? The answer is surely "No." As baby boomers, we probably said we wanted to help others and that we were going to grow up to be nurses, social workers, or teachers. As they say, "Be careful what you wish for, it may come true!"

Looking back on my teen years, I remembered that what I wanted to "do" after graduation was to go away to college. Under that guise, I wanted to go away to a teacher's college. My father's wish was for me to go to the same diploma-nursing program that my mother had graduated from 10 years before her death. Not surprisingly, the program was two miles across town. My plans were to go at least two hours away. I had a full scholarship to the nursing program, so my plans for college were placed on hold. My father's plan for me won out.

I met my husband to be, became a nurse, and became a mother to our son. I had a wonderful career that allowed me to work part time when I needed to be at home more. I worked in every setting in the hospital, except birthing babies. I was a staff nurse and a nurse manager. Along the way, I taught paramedics, oriented critical care nurses, and mentored hundreds of other nurses.

The wish to be a teacher came to the surface. So, at the age of 35, I went to college in the evenings and the weekends, traveling up to 50 miles each way. I joined a sorority. It was an honor's sorority. No wild parties! Such was my luck. And my father's plan won again. But I was able to graduate from a teacher's college with a bachelor's in nursing. Armed with a bachelor's degree, I was more marketable as a nurse. I continued in management, becoming a director of medical-surgical nursing for the same community hospital system where I grew up.

My wish to teach reared up again. I began graduate school, pursuing a degree in family nursing so I would have the credentials to teach nurses. In the middle of getting my masters, our CEO asked to me develop an advocacy program for our hospital system. What better way to be a teacher! To empower patients and their families by giving them knowledge is the ultimate teaching job. My understanding of complex family dynamics has helped me to understand my own family, as well as those that I see daily in my role as the director of patient/family advocacy. How cool is that?

The first moral of this story is "Be careful what you wish for!" It can come true. The second moral is "Father knows best".

Dilemma

The inpatient-nursing unit called me about a bed-rest patient who would not take her pills. The nurses could not figure out what the problem was.

I went to the ward and had a chat with the very pleasant older Asian lady. I worked the conversation to the pill issue; the patient said those pills would not work.

After much discussion, she finally made it clear to me that only room temperature water will work, but what do we give patients? Ice water. After a couple of cups of water to determine the right temperature for the patient, she was satisfied and took her pills.

Don't Mess with God

The triage nurse in the ER paged me with an emergency. When I got to the nurses' station, she hissed, "The priest visiting his mother in curtain 12 just cussed out the psyche doc!"

When I arrived at the room, the priest was calm, stroking his bedridden mother's hair. He explained that while he was administering the rites of the ill, a ritual that takes only a few minutes, the psyche doc barreled into the room and demanded that the priest stop what he was doing so that she could examine the patient. The priest had requested a moment to finish his ritual, which the psyche doc rudely refused. The priest had become agitated and lost his temper. In the process, he told the doctor exactly what he thought of her. She left in a huff and refused to examine the patient for several hours.

Later, after returning to the ER, the psyche doc was bemoaning the terrible way she had been treated by the priest to everyone within earshot. By then, everyone had heard the story, and she wasn't receiving much sympathy. After listening to the doctor go on and on, the medical director, without looking up at her, quietly remarked, "Well, I don't know how you were raised, but I was taught that you don't $%&# with God."

With that, he finished charting and went on to see the next patient, leaving her speechless for the first time all night.

Evelyn's Good Advice

Evelyn, a very young 91 years old, spent more than a week at our hospital, so I had the opportunity to visit her a few times during her stay.

The first time I went to see Evelyn; I noticed that she wasn't watching television, and we chatted about that. She told me that she never watched TV, because there are too many people in the world that need our prayers. She showed me a notebook where she had listed the names of all the people for whom she was praying. (I have to say, I was very pleased when she added my name to her list.)

The last day I visited with Evelyn, I decided to ask her an important question," Evelyn, you have to share with me your secret for living such a long life."

Evelyn smiled and told me about the different ways she had kept active throughout her life. She talked about the long walks she took every day; about the gardens she tended; she talked about waiting for July every year just so she could pick lots of blueberries.

And then she shared with me one of those rare Pearls of Wisdom:

She said, "But I think my husband put it best when he said, "**Evelyn, if ya' just keep movin' they can't bury ya'**.""

Father's Final Gift

An elderly patient was nearing the end of his life during a stay on one of our intensive care units. His son, a minister, was terribly disheartened that his father had never been baptized. In a loving gesture to his boy, the patient consented to baptism – but he was, of course, too sick to leave the hospital to participate in a full body immersion, as their church believed was essential.

We decided to approach the nurse manager of the Burn Unit with an idea: what about "converting" one of the tubs used to debride burn patients into a baptismal fount? Although this notion carried its own risks, all staff, including those from the legal office, was comfortable with the idea.

Much to the relief of his family, the patient was baptized shortly before he died.

Fowl Play

With only my secretary's help I had just started a new patient advocacy program in a 470-bed hospital when I left town to attend a SHCA Board meeting in January.

I called my secretary the next day to discuss issues that had developed since I left; my secretary said, "You won't believe this." She had received a call from a family in the Emergency Department, complaining that there was a rooster in the ER waiting room. The family member then said, "I had to turn off my cell phone but you allow chickens in the building." Very calmly I said, "No, Ma'am, we don't allow chickens in the ER. We'll have someone come and check out the situation."

My secretary is very ingenious. Since she couldn't leave the phones that were ringing off the hook, she asked the director of spiritual care to see if a rooster was indeed in our ER waiting room. The spiritual care director agreed to the task, returning to the office a short time later and informed her that, yes, the rooster was indeed walking around on the floor of the busy ER waiting room. All the family members and patients waiting there were feeding the rooster.

A security guard was dispatched to speak with the owner of the feasting rooster. The patient said she didn't have anyone to leave the rooster with while she came to seek medical attention, and that the rooster was her pride and joy. The security guard was very conscious of good customer service, and asked if the patient could at least keep the rooster inside her coat.

Eventually, the patient was called to the treatment room. The same security guard offered to wait with the rooster outside of the building while the doctor saw the patient. The security guards change locations every two hours, and I was later told that three guards took turns rooster sitting.

The patient was eventually treated and released. She thanked everyone for watching her pet rooster. They both left in good spirits and health.

I have told the rooster story to many new associates at orientation. This is truly an example of good customer service. Security certainly thought outside the box (or maybe the coop) to delight the patient in this instance.

Frank's Story

A male volunteer named Frank has been with me since the creation of the patient advocacy program in 1994. Frank loves patient advocacy and often goes the extra mile in helping patients. My favorite story involves a patient that I will call Mr. Harris, who had a massive stroke.

When Frank presented his visit list to the patient care facilitator for approval, she told him that Mr. Harris had a massive stroke and was unable to communicate. She said she would leave the choice of whether or not to visit up to Frank. After much thought, Frank decided to see Mr. Harris.

Frank knocked, entered the room and introduced himself, but he was unable to make eye contact with the patient. Frank described the process for expressing complaints with no direct response from Mr. Harris. Occasionally, Mr. Harris would speak, but it was impossible to determine what he was saying. Frank then told Mr. Harris all about himself and his family.

After several minutes, Frank touched Mr. Harris on the arm and told him that he was leaving to visit other patients but would leave a brochure on the table. Frank nearly got to the door when he heard a voice distinctly say, "Don't go!" He turned around and asked Mr. Harris, "Did you speak to me?" Mr. Harris nodded his head yes.

Frank sat by the bed for nearly an hour listening to Mr. Harris go through periods of "gibberish" interspersed with describing how his wife had died at our hospital six months before. Mr. Harris said his only child was a daughter who was a single mother that lived several hours away, so he had no one to visit him.

Frank came back to see Mr. Harris several times during the next week and visited him when he was discharged to a nursing home, where he died. Frank said on his last visit to the nursing home, Mr. Harris could not speak but held tightly to his hand.

Funeral Dentures

It seems sometimes that we are tooth fairies, either rummaging through dirty laundry to find those missing dentures, or making arrangements with the local dentists to have dentures replaced. Sometimes, the dentures materialize shortly after discharge, saving us a lot of trouble.

This was what happened when the dentures of a recently deceased patient mysteriously appeared in the Guest Relations office. Relieved that we were not going to have to replace a set of teeth for a dead person, we sent the teeth on to the funeral home.

A week or so later, we received a grateful call from the patient's daughter. "Thank you so much for giving my mama teeth to be buried in! She never could afford dentures while she was alive, and it was so kind of you to give her some for her funeral!"

Furby* Lady

"Your nurses killed my mother!" These were the first words I heard
w h e n I answered the phone. The ensuing conversation lasted over an
hour, we discussed how saddened the caller was at losing her mother to
cancer, the anger she felt towards her mother's family; the stuffed toy
moose that the family gave her mother that eventually killed her with the
poisonous gases it breathed in her room; the voices she heard all the time,
and her latest stint as a patient in a psyche facility.

Feeling much better at the end of the conversation, the woman asked me
to please call the other side of her family and ask them to leave her alone
forever. I explained that my role was to facilitate complaint management
relative to hospital business, not mediate family conflict unrelated to the
hospital. She agreed, and thanked me for the time I spent on the phone
with her.

The next day, I picked up my voice mail between patient visits, and had
one that lasted as long as the system allowed. The caller from the day
before cursed at me and she cursed at the hospital. She cursed at her
mother's family and she cursed at the voices in her head. "You killed
my mother!!! Your nurses didn't care! You killed my mother!!!"
Needless to say, I wasn't very excited about returning that phone call.

Ten minutes later, I received another voice mail, again lasting as long as
allowed. This time, the same woman sounded like a different person
when she apologized profusely for calling me names, cursing and blaming
the hospital for her mother's death. She told me how she'd been hearing
voices, and that the medicine she took for the voices wasn't helping. She
tried to out-distance the voices by driving as fast as she could to get away
from them, but it just didn't work. Finally, in a fit of anger and
frustration, she stopped the car at a pay phone and called me.

After her temper tantrum on my voice mail, she turned to her van and began tearing through it, throwing everything inside out on the ground. The voices were getting louder, she said, until she finally found out where they were really coming from. "There was a FURBY in the back seat!!!" She proudly informed the voice mail. I never heard from her again.

*A Furby is a toy that was quite popular about seven years ago. It is equipped with a mechanism that allows it to sense movement and sounds, and it responds with whirrs, trills, coos, sighs and giggles at the slightest sound or motion. Children can teach it to "sleep", but most parents found that removing the batteries or bashing it on the head with a hammer worked best.

George

I live and work in Northern Maine, far away from the part of Maine known for fishing, lobsters and tourism. Up here we grow potatoes, broccoli, and soy, and have a large forestry population – folks who "work in the woods". Sometimes there seem to be as many moose as people. Life is quiet here. The folks are conservative and neighborly. Our communities help raise our children and look out for our senior citizens.

This county has four hospitals. The one where I work, the largest, was the only one to receive flu vaccines this year. In response, we split the serum into four parts and gave equal amounts to each hospital to inoculate high-risk patients. The four hospitals ran concurrent clinics on two consecutive Saturdays. The first clinic is for children and pregnant w o m e n , and the second Saturday is for senior citizens and adults with chronic medical issues. These clinics were efficient and well run.

This morning I received a phone call from a 75-year-old gentleman who had attended Saturday's clinic; we'll call him George. I believe George is a lonely older man who really just wanted someone to talk to so, of course, the switchboard patched him over to my office.

George began our conversation by introducing himself. He then told me his story. He came in on Saturday for a flu shot, and was sitting in "the big room" next to another man and his wife. (I later learned George's wife is in a nursing home). He told me that all of a sudden a young girl walked in, probably in her late 20's-early 30's, wearing jeans and a beige jacket wide open with nothing on underneath it.

Both he and the guy next to him were staring, of course, so the guy's wife hit him on the head with a newspaper. George said, "Boy, I'm glad my wife's not here to hit me", so the woman came over and hit him on the head with the newspaper too.

George asked the young woman what she was doing there, and she said she was transporting seniors for their flu shots. He asked her why she was dressed like that, and she said it was to give all the old folks a thrill!

I asked if she was an employee of our hospital, and he said she wasn't. I apologized on behalf of the hospital if he was offended, but he said he certainly wasn't offended.

I asked if he would like me to make this issue into a formal complaint, and he said, "Heck, I'm not complaining! I'm 75 years old! I just thought someone should know!" I could hear the smile in his voice. *

George went on to tell me he was trying to bake bread, and asked if I ever baked bread. He told me he added too much hot water and killed the yeast last time, so this time he was using a thermometer. He told me he goes to Florida for the winter, and talked about his trips. He even told me how to use powdered milk to make the refrigerated kind last longer. He seemed like a very dear man.

I knew I had to get back to work, so after chatting for about 20 minutes I asked George if he was sure he didn't want me to write up a complaint. He chuckled and politely declined, but asked what my job entailed. I gave him a thumbnail description and he responded, "Oh, so you're the fence mender." I said that I guess sometimes I am. I politely said goodbye to George and made sure he had my contact information if he ever needed my services, because you just never know.

*Incidentally, since no one else saw this young woman, I suspect it was a girl in a beige jacket and tight beige shirt. She sure did get George's attention.

Growing into the Important Role of Patient Advocate

I was new in my position as patient representative. I worked the evening shift and every other weekend. My position was created primarily to keep patients informed in our Emergency Room.
There was some direction for what I was supposed to do, but I was refining the job every day.

I learned early on, from a very difficult case, what was important to families when faced with a crisis in our Emergency Room.
The patient was a 72 year-old male who came in with a diagnosis of chest pain. When he arrived in our emergency room, he was conscious and alert but suddenly went into V-tac and had to be coded. We were able to get him back into a normal heart rhythm. His wife arrived shortly after this, and the ER physician came in to speak to her only briefly because t he patient coded again. It was obvious at this time that he was unstable. We needed to get him to ICU to begin drips and better assess his heart.

The wife was not able to see him, since everything was happening so fast. I stayed with her and told her I would keep her informed and get her in to see him as soon as we could. I knew by what was happening that I would need to do this quickly. I brought the wife to our ICU waiting room and went back into ICU. The patient was in V-tac again, and once again we were able to get him out. I knew I needed to get the wife back to see her husband as soon as possible due to his irritable heart. Instead of asking the nursing staff I told the nurses I was doing this.

I brought the wife back to see her husband. He was conscious and alert. They spoke for a moment. She held his hand and told him she loved him. He went into V-tac again, so I had to bring the wife back to the ICU waiting room. This time the patient did not make it. I remained with the wife when the physician came to give her the bad news and stayed with her until more family came. I stayed with the wife and the families until all their questions were answered and their good byes were said.

From a letter I received from the wife two months later, I learned how much it meant to her that she had been allowed to see her husband and tell him she loved him one last time. This truly touched my heart, and I realized that I had done the right thing. I do believe I already knew this due to my own personal circumstances. On the day my father died in an out of state hospital, when I was eleven, I did not have the opportunity to speak to him on the phone and tell him I loved him. To this day, that still stays with me.

I believe that our own personal experiences, negative or positive, play a role in how we handle situations we are faced with as patient representatives every day. I know in my heart and share this with my staff that we need to focus on doing the right thing.

It has taught me how to be a liaison to our patients and their families.

Halloween Angel

One Halloween, I was visiting some patients on the pediatric ward when I came to a room with a very sick little boy in the bed. His parents had been staying with him pretty much around the clock. Sitting by her brother's bed was a little girl dressed in an angel costume. She actually looked like a little angel, costume or not, but she looked so sad.

It seems she didn't know if she was going to be able to go trick- or-treating. Her parents weren't sure about leaving their sick son. I asked them if I could take her trick-or-treating around the hospital. The parents were happy to be able to let her go, so I told them I would come back to pick the little girl up in a half-hour. Then I went back to my office and called around to different areas of the hospital, explaining the situation, and asking for help; my co-workers more than happy to lend a hand.

When I picked the little girl up, we went trick-or-treating in several departments in the hospital, all of which had something special to give h e r . She didn't have anything to put her goodies in, so Lisa in the business office gave her a plastic pumpkin that had been sitting on her desk. Admitting staff gave her two cupcakes from their party, one of which the angel said she would save for her brother. The gift shop volunteers added to her pumpkin, also. Everyone seemed eager to give her a happy Halloween!

And now our little angel was smiling!

Handling Miss Daisy

I got paged "STAT" to our atrium area, which is right inside the front door of the medical center. When I arrived, I saw a very well dressed elderly woman in a wheel chair yelling, "You goons get away from me! Stay back!" to three police officers and a cab driver. I knelt down by the lady's wheel chair so I could speak with her at eye level. She yelled, "Don't touch my chair". I said, "I am sorry, let's just move closer to this bench so I can sit down and speak with you." As we spoke the story began to unravel.

I will call her Ms. Daisy, and she was very much like the lady in the movie, Driving Ms. Daisy. Ms. Daisy had gotten up that morning in the nursing home where she lived, got all dressed up and called a cab from a nearby town. She instructed the driver to take her to a local bank where she withdrew several hundred dollars to come to our urban medical center for a doctor's appointment. She was very angry because now she was being told that she did not have an appointment with anyone at the hospital.

After many phone calls to the nursing home, the supervisor, the owner of the cab company, the driver and I were able to give Ms. Daisy a choice of options. She finally decided she would get back into the cab and return to her room at the nursing home.
All of this took place as one security officer stayed in the wings until Ms. Daisy had made her choice and was safely back in the taxicab.

The cab driver and the dispatcher were both new and unaware that this particular nursing home patient often called for a cab, and when she did, they were not to send a driver, but to contact the nursing staff instead. Thank God the cab driver didn't just drop her off assuming that she was correct. Ms. Daisy was returned safely to her room at the nursing home.

The patient advocate awaited the next crisis of the day.

Happy Anniversary

One of my favorite customer service stories involved a very elderly married couple that was admitted on the same floor. The housekeeper for the area discovered that the two were celebrating their 73rd wedding anniversary the next day. The housekeeping department called me to see if something could be done for the couple.

An event this rare and special should not be celebrated in a hospital, but the couple's conditions warranted it. In response, we banned together with nursing and food services staff to make plans. Arrangements were made for a special lunch for the two patients and their daughter, featuring steak, lobster tail and a special cake to celebrate the occasion, all modified to meet their dietary restraints. We purchased a card for staff to sign, a big bouquet of balloons and, as luck would have it, an incredible arrangement of roses from our gift shop.

The couple's daughter visited with mom while staff brought her husband down the hall so they could visit together. Meanwhile, members from the unit, housekeeping, food service, the gift shop, and me, hid nearby waiting to present their anniversary feast and gifts. Once the couple was settled we paraded in with bright balloons flying and hugs and good wishes to the "bride & groom". The absolute surprise on their faces was priceless! Tears formed in everyone's eyes as we left the couple to enjoy their special occasion in privacy.

A couple weeks later a card arrived from the blushing bride, who thanked us for making their anniversary so special. She said they never expected to celebrate it in such a festive manner and in the presence of such good friends. She said that she would never forget how we made it their anniversary such a very special time. Sadly, she wrote, it was also their last anniversary as her husband passed away just a few days after their special party.

As you can imagine, policy and procedures did not cover throwing a party for two elderly patients and there was no budget for roses and lobster. However, doing things from the heart is more important than worrying about rules or a few dollars. It's impossible for any of us to know how a caring touch, a thoughtful gesture or a kind word will forever imprint itself on someone's heart.

Perhaps our actions made a lasting impression on our patient, but I know her simple thanks made a permanent one on me.

Harold

I received a call from Harold in March 2001. He had recently moved from Indiana to Texas, transferring his healthcare to the facility in his new community. I can't recall exactly why Harold called me, but I do remember his request was very modest and I was easily able to accommodate him. I also recall that Harold expressed deep gratitude for my small act and so, during our brief discussion, we became friends.

A few days later I received a letter from Harold, again thanking me for my previous "kind and thoughtful assistance" in resolving his concern. He also included a poem, "Look To This Day," stating he had written it for my family, my friends, and me. I was so touched by his expression of gratitude that at my last state conference as the local consumer advocates chapter president, I gave copies of Harold's poem to my officers and board members, noting that the poem was my expression of gratitude to them for all of their efforts during the previous two years.

I hope you enjoy Harold's words and thoughts as much as I did.

Look to This Day

Look to this day for it is life,
The very life of life.
In its brief course lie all the realities
and verities of existence.
The bliss of growth,
The splendor of action,
The glory of power.
For yesterday is but a dream
And tomorrow is only a vision.
But today, well lived,
Makes every yesterday a dream of happiness,
And every tomorrow a vision of hope.
Look well, therefore, to this day.

--Harold

Heart as Big as a Box

Rhonda had left a voice mail about Michael that made me cry. Charles called to inform me that the grandmother was not to be trusted. Jodie stopped me in the hall to warn me that Ed's last check bounced. The chaplain knocked at my office door to tell me Cameron is signed up for hospice.

Amy paged me so that I might come to the seventh floor to calm down a family in conference room B. On the complaint hotline, Sean insists the doctor is scheduling needless surgery for Lauren, and he wants it stopped. Karen pinned me against the wall to tell me that she called for a wheelchair at 9, 10, and here it is after 11 and still no wheelchair. Funny, how even with the press of people in street clothes, lab coats, scrubs and uniforms, the cafeteria offers a quiet retreat.

Over mac and cheese Brent and I discuss why the database might have started numbering the complaints in a puzzling random order and the possible remedies.

Pat left a sticky note on my monitor, while I was at lunch, announcing that the Johnsons don't have a penny left to their name and are in need of a parking pass and meal vouchers. Julie tells me that Nate's parents just might look me up this afternoon, and if I need security backup any time during the conversation, don't hesitate to call 7777.

Chris replied by e-mail that, yes, it is true, the next available clinic appointment for a new patient is 146 days out. A well- padded envelope holds a nine page letter with that many typeset bullets stating why the parents expect an adjustment to Jason's behavior health bill; they CCed the Daily Standard.

Time to go home. Wait. A flashing light on the phone catches my eye, tempting me. OK, I'll listen. But I'm not making a call back. A mother, twin boys, she mentions autism. Tears are in her voice. Tears of relief; patience and understanding shown her boys exceeds all expectations.

Humm. Someone has a heart as big as a box. Hasn't this day been grand!

He Just Wanted to Teach Her a Lesson

I was called to the ICCU waiting area to talk with a lady who was very upset. It seems that she had cashed her husband's paycheck before coming to the hospital. She had been waiting with other family members and, at some point, had gone to the cafeteria with them. When she got to the cafeteria she discovered the money was missing from her purse. She insisted that someone, probably a staff person, had stolen her money.

We backtracked throughout the hospital. We had security and multiple other staff people looking for her money. She was frantic. We spent a half hour scouring every conceivable location and asking people if they had seen anyone with or near her purse. I was at my wits end because we really had no proof that she had come into the facility with the cash.

I finally suggested that she come to my office and call the police to institute a report. At that point, her husband, who had been present, but much uninvolved, spoke up and said, "Well, I have her money. She always goes off and leaves it open where anyone can get into it. I just wanted to teach her a lesson."

Well, it may be funny now, but it sure wasn't then!

Healing Powers of Music

Heart transplant recipient Mr. O'Neil began to have difficulty following several years of good health. His family was thankful for the time that the transplant had afforded him, but realized, as he lay connected to life support that his days were short. Mr.
O'Neil was very restless, but became less anxious when one of the music therapists was rounding, playing the guitar and singing for patients.

His family invited the musician into the room so their loved one could hear the music more clearly. The family was so pleased to have found a diversion that seemed to make their loved one rest more peacefully.

As the family was talking with the musician, they learned that this person actually worked in the cath lab at the hospital and ha d been using his breaks and lunchtime to volunteer as a music therapist. They also learned that this volunteer program did not have the funds to keep the program going and that they had not had a regular program in some time. However, this employee enjoyed using his God-given talent to bring a little joy to patients and their families. The family was quite impressed with this gentleman's compassion and generosity.

The following day, after a care-conference between the patient's family and caregivers, it was decided to disconnect the patient from life support. Once again the patient was quite restless, and the family was concerned that their loved one would struggle through his final breaths. Prior to disconnecting Mr. O'Neil from life support, the family asked if their new friend, the musician, was working today and if so, could he possibly come and play for their father.

Much to their delight, the staff member was just finishing up a case in the catheterization lab and was able to quickly grab his guitar and be there just as the staff was preparing to disconnect this dear gentleman from the equipment that was keeping his heart beating. Almost immediately, Mr. O'Neil seemed to relax as he listened to beautiful hymns being played and sung. While listening to the musician play his second piece, Mr. O'Neil very peacefully slipped from this earth to his new heavenly home.

The family was so grateful for this gentleman's gift of music, love, and compassion that they asked him to sing at their father's funeral. The staff member was deeply touched by being included during this special time for their family. This staff member continues to volunteer his time to bring a little joy to patients who are ill and in the hospital. He says this is what makes his job so special.

Help Wanted: Notary

My story is regarding a family that I helped within the first six months of my career as a patient rep. I had never done this type of work before so every situation was very new.

One of my duties is as notary public. I had received a call from the family members of a patient in the hospital. They were very upset that they were not receiving any information from the physician and staff about the patient's care. I explained to them that because of HIPAA the patient needed to sign a consent form. The family decided who would be on the consent form and I went with them to witness the signature.

Because of the patient's medical problems, he had a difficult time signing the paper. The daughter had to help him do this. I saw that it was hard on her and tried to offer as much support as possible. Eventually he was able to sign the paper and they were grateful for my help.

The next day when I came in to work, there was a box of doughnuts on my desk along with a note of thanks from the daughter. (I still have that note in my possession.)

The following day the family decided to have some financial paperwork notarized. They called me again and I went to the room to assist with this. Again there was difficulty in getting the paper signed. It was a very emotional time for both the family members and me. We were finally able to complete the papers and I went back to my office.

When I came into work the next day I found out that the patient had passed away in the early morning. I hurried down to the unit to see if the family was still in the hospital.

They were in with the social worker making arrangements when I popped into the office. The daughter was so happy that I had stopped by to see them. She gave me a huge hug and thanked me for all that I had done.

About a month later, this daughter wrote a two-page letter to our administration complimenting me and letting them know how helpful I was to them. They also thanked a variety of the staff that had helped the patient. I will never forget this patient or his family, as this was my first experience with the loss of a patient.

I Found My Calling

He had been receiving life-sustaining treatments for a long time and finally reached the point where he felt ready to let go. He called all his family together (they traveled here from different states) to tell them of his decision to stop receiving treatments and to say his good-byes.

I had only been working as a patient advocate for a few weeks when I first met this family. They were sitting in the courtyard of the hospital. It was a warm, balmy summer evening and it seemed like any typical family gathering together for a reunion. There were some tears, but there was also lots of laughter.

The following day the patient's wife and daughters asked to speak with me in private. One of the daughters shared with me that her father had seemed so at peace with himself when he originally told them of his decision. While they were naturally saddened at the thought of him dying, they respected his decision and did not want to see him suffering any more pain.

Apparently after this original meeting with his family, the doctor had suggested to their father that he try another treatment and now her father said he was very confused and emotional and didn't want to talk about it (to his family) anymore. The family shared that they thought he felt obligated to the doctor to try again, but he really did not want to. They felt he might speak to me, being an outsider, and asked if I would try talking to him. He agreed to see me and I went to his room.

Through a veil of tears he told me he was a retired minister, and with the help of God he had made his decision to die a natural death. He said he was so grateful for all the doctor had done for him, but he felt the time had come to let go and now he was feeling that maybe he owed it to his doctor to try one more time. He said everything had seemed so clear in his mind and he felt at peace with himself and his family, and now another hurdle was being thrown in front of him.

I asked him "for this moment, excluding all of the doctors, your family and everyone else, what do you think is the right thing for you to do?" He squeezed my hand and said, "I want to go". I asked him if he would like me to relay that to his doctor and he replied, "Yes." I squeezed his hand in response and told him "Goodnight and God Bless."

The following day he went home, and with the assistance of Hospice he died peacefully surrounded by his family a week later.

I knew I had found my calling!

If You Wish Upon a Star

After Andrew was admitted for orthopedic surgery, he reported that his belongings were missing. Because patient advocates are most skilled at finding these lost objects, I analyzed the situation and researched his prior room assignments. When I uncovered that he was originally assigned to another room, I checked that room and, as I suspected, his belongings were there. I quickly returned the bag to Andrew; he checked it and confirmed that everything was there. His pleasure at having his possessions returned was quite obvious.

The next day I received a call from one of Andrew's friends. I thought he was calling to thank me for finding the missing items. However, he indicated that Andrew had some questions regarding his surgery and, by the way, his lower denture had been found in his stomach.

I was stunned by this information and was sure it had to be a mistake. I reviewed Andrew's chart and found out that he had experienced chest pain and had a cardiac cath. The test revealed an item that looked like railroad tracks imprinted with a star. Further examination revealed it to be Andrew's lower denture. An endoscopy was scheduled; the denture was removed and returned.

I met with Andrew to follow up, and was amused that he did not seem at all surprised by the outcome. He simply took it in stride and said how happy he was that his denture had been located and returned. In fact, he gave me a big smile to show me the denture had been returned to its rightful location! He was not sure when he had swallowed the denture and didn't reported it lost until it was discovered during the catheterization. He told me the denture had a star for identification purposes.

So when dentures get lost, be sure to check all the usual places...food trays, wastebaskets, and laundry. But from now on, you may have one additional place to check!

It Takes A Team

I had only been a patient relations coordinator for six months, when a patient advocate located in another state, telephoned me to share that his father-in-law had suffered a heart attack while on vacation, and that he was currently receiving care in our facility. The patient advocate asked me to visit his mother-in-law, as she was in her 80s, in an unfamiliar city, and he was concerned for her as well as his father-in-law.

The patient had suffered a heart attack while waiting to see an area performer and was airlifted to our facility. Out of kindness, a local resident had driven the mother-in-law to our facility, where she was now staying in one of our hospitality rooms. The room just happened to be right down the hall from my office.

After receiving the call, I first contacted our nursing staff to check on the patient. He was recovering from his heart attack and seemed to be doing well for his age. I then met and introduced myself to his wife of over 50 years. We enjoyed each other's company, as I explained she could just "adopt" me as her granddaughter until her family arrived from her home state. I visited with her daily – making sure she had food passes for our cafeteria and money to call home.

One morning, though, she was not in her hospitality room. Staff could see my concerned expression and gave me the news that the prior evening, she too, had suffered a heart attack! After her procedure, our loving staff in the cardiac unit placed both patients together.

I was now able to visit with them both and I came to truly understand how each member of our team is necessary in all aspects of patient care to make it work. Staff members from housekeeping, nursing, physicians, and patient relations all came to love this couple.

Unfortunately, my story does not have a happy ending. The father-in-law, who generously shared his humor with us, passed away. Family was by his wife's side immediately to help ease her ache (and ours) and to take her safely home.

I've never spoken to her since, but three years later her face, their love for one another, and our team effort as a health care system, still gives me spirit to keep giving to our patients and their loved ones.

Lend a Helping Eye

Frank, a patient advocate volunteer, visited Mrs. Jones, a visually impaired woman on the medical unit. During the course of their conversation, Mrs. Jones said the thing she missed the most about losing her sight was not being able to read the newspaper. She said she listened to the radio and TV but did not get the "juicy local gossip" from the local newspaper.

That night, Frank gathered a week's worth of The Post, the local newspaper. The next day, he came to Mrs. Jones' room and spent two hours reading all the local news to her. Mrs. Jones was so delighted that she told everyone who came to see her about the kind and caring patient advocate.

Little Things Mean a Lot

They say that physicians who end up being patients are the most difficult of all. I have not found this to be true. Their expectations are higher simply because they know what we are capable of.

Dr. Morris was one such patient. He is an oncologist at our hospital, and was very ill with a disease they weren't sure could be cured. As days went by, he became thinner and more sickly- looking than I could ever have imagined. Since his wife is an oncology nurse, she was acutely aware of his deterioration.

I visited with Dr. Morris at his bedside because he was unhappy with the treatment he was receiving from his attending physician. He was correct – his attending doc was violating his right to refuse high-dose corticosteroids. Through the days Dr. Morris and I spoke of medicine, human nature, and manners. We became fast friends.

One day, while sitting next to his bed, he asked where I had gotten an American flag pin I customarily wore on my ID badge. It's a pin reminiscent of the bars worn by soldiers. It looks like a flag; American flag fabric covers it. It is one of my very favorites. I told him and his wife that I had gotten it at a VA booth at a Health Fair sponsored by our hospital. I looked at him lying in that bed and my heart hurt. I did the only thing I felt I could do to help him. I unclipped my pin and pinned it to his jonnie. He was flabbergasted.

His wife told me she could write and get one. I told her, "So could I". Dr. Morris told me in a cracked voice that he was once a soldier and has always admired my pin.

Dr. Morris not only survived his disease, but is now back full time in his oncology practice. I can't help but smile whenever I see him walking through the hall in his white coat, standing upright and strong, and a picture of health. I usually see him with his wife as they head to the cafeteria, and each time, after smiling and greeting them, I notice the flag pin, proudly displayed on his lapel...and I smile again.

Lost Treasure

Our hospital has a safe where patient valuables are placed for safekeeping. Sometimes valuables are not claimed and these items are given to the patient representative so they can be returned to the patient or family.

One day, I was given a number of envelopes containing unclaimed valuables. One of the envelopes was very heavy and fell out of the pile, so that seemed like a good place to start. As I looked up the name of the patient on the envelope, I discovered that the patient had expired. I continued to search for a relative until I finally found the name and phone number of the patient's daughter.

I called the daughter, introduced myself and told her why I had called. When she asked me what was in the envelope, I opened it and found a man's ring, containing a large dark stone surrounded by multiple diamonds. I quickly explained my findings to the daughter.

Moments passed in silence until I asked if she was still on the line. As she began talking, she explained that she had just finished watching a television program about how family members have found missing valuables of loved ones who have passed on by channeling with them. She went on to say that she had just watched the program and was thinking about her fat he r's ring when I called.

The daughter came over that same day to pick up her father's ring. I have never seen a broader smile in my life...except possibly my own, for being a small part of this special experience.

Luna the Wonder Horse

I am the customer service manager at the town medical center. We are very customer oriented at our hospital. We try to instill in all of our staff that they are all patient representatives, and that when they see a need, they should try to do something about it. That is what happened in the following story.

We had a patient on medical/oncology that was very, very sick. Her prognosis was not very good. She was a relatively young woman who rode horses. She loved her horse, Luna, and had missed her terribly since being in the hospital.

Her husband brought Luna to the field behind the hospital, so that his wife could look at her from the window of her 2nd floor room. John, one of our security guards, happened to see how much this meant to the patient, and thought how much more it might help, if she could see Luna up close and touch her. John talked to the husband to see if he would like them to bring the horse to the back entrance of the hospital and bring the patient down to see, touch, and spend time with her beloved horse.

The husband took to the idea immediately and made plans for a family friend to bring the horse to the hospital. John worked out the logistics with the medical/oncology director and other hospital employees (including myself). The horse was brought to the hospital, the patient was wheeled down and out the back door, and the patient was able to spend 20-30 precious minutes with her horse.

The patient had been lying around sleeping a lot and had not been very responsive when awake. But as soon as she saw Luna, she talked and sang to the horse, petted her, and hugged her. We took pictures with a Polaroid camera to hang on the wall in her room – pictures that she could look at and enjoy.
After she was returned to her room, she was much happier, more alert, and was actually hungry for the first time in days!

All this because a security guard happened to see a need and took action to respond to that need.

Maggie and George

The charge nurse on 5W called to see if I could visit with the wife of the patient in room 532. The patient had been diagnosed with a UTI and was under the care of the inpatient physician service. His wife was complaining about him being cared for by strangers. She was monopolizing the staff when they were swamped with other patients. The nurse asked me to speak with the woman and try to assuage her fears.

I arrived in room 532 to visit with George and Maggie. George had had a stroke some years before. His employer required him to retire from his truck-driving job. He was confused and unable to ambulate or speak, a n d had been almost completely bedridden for six years. Maggie had become his primary caregiver, and they were soon to celebrate their 48th wedding anniversary.

When looking at Maggie, I noticed that she was fidgety and her shoulders were tight. During the course of our conversation, she would pat her sleeping husband's hand and adjust his covers, her eyes darting from me back to him to check his status. She reminded me of a mother guarding her wounded child. The fearful determination reflected on her face let me know she taken the position of defending her man.

As we talked about her life with George, and this hospitalization, it became clear that Maggie's concern about the inpatient physician had nothing to do with the doctor's competence or behavior. He had correctly diagnosed the UTI and prescribed medication that was proving effective. His manner had been polite and he had taken time to listen to her concerns.

Her complaint was not about nursing care either – the nurses had displayed great care for George. Maggie just didn't like the idea that George was in stranger's hands. Out of fear that George's needs would go unmet, she had written on the whiteboard above the bed, "CAN'T TALK" "CAN'T WALK" "CONFUSED" in bold letters.

I explained the function of the inpatient rounding service and assured Maggie that the physicians were well trained. I encouraged her to speak to George's PCP about her concerns, and I told her to contact the charge nurse, as well. I gave her my card with instructions to call me if she needed assistance. Still, I could sense that her anxiety had not been relieved. The fidgeting continued. She looked at me warily. She needed something more.

Something about good patient care I had just learned at a SHCA conference popped into my head. I excused myself and went to the whiteboard.

At the top of the board, I wrote, "GEORGE" in bold letters. In one corner, I added "RETIRED TRUCK DRIVER."

"How many kids do you have?" I asked. "Five – We have five kids," she answered, quietly. "5 CHILDREN" went on the whiteboard

"Grandkids?" "Eleven. And one great-grandchild!" I could hear the excitement in her voice. I added these to the whiteboard.

"What does George like to do?" "Well, he loves music and reading...and he plays checkers and chess!" "LOVES MUSIC AND READING" "PLAYS CHECKERS AND CHESS" both went on the whiteboard.

"There," I said, and put the pen down. I turned around and looked at Maggie. The fidgeting had stopped and her shoulders were relaxed. She beamed as she looked at the board that reflected the George she knew and loved. With tears in her eyes, she smiled and said, "It's gonna be okay - he's a person again!"

I had gone to room 532 to educate the wife of a patient. I left there having learned the importance of really knowing the person in the bed. I looked at my watch. Our interaction had taken a whopping 15 minutes.

Epilogue: George returned to our facility for the last time three months later. Maggie had specifically asked that he be brought here – so he could die among friends.

Make Someone Happy

I have often told people how lucky I am to be a patient advocate. It is such a privilege to help people work through their problems. And it's such a joy to be able to brighten someone's day by staying with him or her during a difficult time in his or her life. By holding their hand, getting them a small gift, offering them a few kind words, or simply listening.

Sometimes, while I'm listening, I'm amazed at people's ability to maintain a positive attitude in the midst of tremendous adversity. As I talked to Barbara about her upcoming open-heart surgery, I found out that she was currently undergoing physical therapy for knee surgery. She also talked about the daughter she had lost to cerebral palsy. You could hear the tremendous love and pride in her voice as she talked about:

- The loving teacher that fought to get her daughter into a regular classroom when she was ready for high school.
- The device that was invented so that she could communicate with her eyes.
- The grades that were good enough to get her on the honor roll.
- The "I Love You Day" that the school held for her before she graduated.

The boy that became her best friend and took her to school dances – including the senior prom. She would arrive at these dances in a wheelchair, and her friend would pick her up and dance with her in his arms.

When the staff noticed that Maggie, one of our elderly patients, wasn't getting any visitors, they called me. I know Maggie appreciated my visits and the bouquet of red and white carnations I brought her for Valentine's Day; but her pleasure couldn't compare to the joy I experienced listening to her wonderful stories. While visiting with the elderly, I have discovered a secret...they have so many marvelous things to share.

I spent two hours with Aimee one afternoon listening to all the health problems she's experienced over the years and suddenly felt very grateful. Why was I so blessed? Why had I sidestepped all the misery that Aimee faced every day? When I found out that the hospital didn't have any fragrance-free soap and Aimee couldn't use anything that contained a fragrance, I went out and bought a gift bag and filled it with her favorite soap. She was delighted with this small gift. And the hospital, of course, now stocks fragrance-free soap on its shelves.

As patient advocates, we get to hand out meal tickets, phone cards, and other small tokens – and we learn to keep lots of Kleenex close by. We get to be there when our patients are going through life changing illnesses. We get to bring understanding to situations and comfort those who are afraid.

The Golden Rule suggests that we treat others the way we would like to be treated ourselves. The platinum rule suggests we go a step further and treat others as THEY want to be treated. An old song tells us, "Make someone happy, and you will be happy too."

Making a Difference

Coming to a children's psychiatric hospital from a large medical center as a patient and family advocate, I certainly expected the role to be different in some ways. Many issues were the same, but it was clear there are aspects of advocacy unique to mental health treatment. Particularly in children, mental health problems and disorders require very sensitive treatment, as well as the courage and commitment of families, and the care and concern of the hospital staff. I never cease to be impressed at the levels of commitment I see from both family and medical staff.

I was recently contacted by a facility doctor about an adolescent who was in treatment with us. A young mother, the teen was in serious financial need; she and her baby were living in an apartment without any furniture.

Knowing that our hospital staff members are very generous in their help, I sent out an email to all staff that there was a small family in need of beds, mattresses and basic household furniture and goods. I was amazed at the response – I had offers of many beds, entire bedroom sets, and a range of items from vacuum cleaners to a kitchen set. The most touching donation was
$1000 that came from a parent of one of our staff members for the family to buy new beds and mattresses.

It was incredibly gratifying to witness the outpouring of help and support, and to be able to help make a real difference for one family.

Mr. Easton Dies

Once I was a real nurse who took care of patients. The place where I worked was a hospital, not a "health care provider." My business was caring, and the bottom line was someone else's problem. My career t o o k a path that lead me away from the bedside, but one patient brought me back.

Dashing down the hallway, behind schedule as usual, I am tempted to ignore the man in room 415 as he gestures frantically for my attention. Our eyes lock and his fear is a magnet that pulls at the core of my being, reminding me that I didn't choose a career in nursing to rush from one meeting to another. I step into his room.

"I'm...I can't...." He doesn't have to say any more. I pull a stethoscope out of the pocket of my lab coat and listen to his chest, and then adjust the flow meter above his bed to deliver more oxygen through the tube that leads to his nose. Positioning the pillows behind him so that the extra oxygen might actually do him some good, I see Mr. Easton relax a bit. My hand goes to his forehead, a mother's trick that works well for nurses too. His face is pink and sweaty from the effort of breathing, and in his pale, watery eyes I see gratitude.

"Damned nurse out there," he sputters in the peevish tones of a man with a chronic lung disorder for whom breathing is a constant, tiresome struggle. "A man could die and no one would notice." His is an all-too-common complaint. It's not the nurse's fault, but I don't bother to explain that to Mr. Easton. Every patient on the floor is at least as sick as he is, and the nurses can only do so much. "Well, you didn't die. I'm right here, and if you calm down a bit, you'll feel better."

A quick peek at my watch tells me that the budget meeting has started without me. If I don't hurry I'll miss my last opportunity to plead my case before the budget is finalized, yet I decide to stay with Mr. Easton. I drop into the chair beside his bed and reach for his hand. He folds his fingers around mine. They're cold and the nail beds are blue.

"You know where I'll be this weekend?" he asks me. The extra oxygen and my presence have calmed him so that he can speak without fighting for air. "Probably right here," I respond, thinking he's talking about going home. That's all everyone wants. It's all I want sometimes. "Nope. I'll be at Forrest Lawn in Long Beach," he replies.

I look into his eyes and glimpse the man he was before his illness robbed him of his strength and merriment, forcing him into a shell of fear and anxiety. "I'll bet you'll be right here celebrating Father's Day with your children on Sunday," I tell him, but I know he's probably right. Dying people know these things. We chat for a while and he falls asleep still clutching my hand. His hand is warm now, and the warmth fills me with peace. I am where I belong.

After a while I slip out of the room and take Mr. Easton's chart from the rack in the nurse's station. I am dismayed to find that he is a "full code," meaning that if he gets worse, it could be necessary to prolong the misery that has become his life by performing CPR. I page his doctor thinking that perhaps he'd forgotten to write the Do Not Resuscitate order that would spare Mr. Easton that final assault. My page isn't answered, and my mind turns to the three o'clock staff meeting and the mountain of paperwork under which my desk is buried.

Late that night thoughts of Mr. Easton are woven through the thin fabric of my dreams. I was never able to speak to his doctor. "You can take care of it in the morning," I tell myself, as I struggle toward a deeper state of sleep.

At eight the next morning, I stop in to check on Mr. Easton and find that he isn't his usual cantankerous, breathless self. His face is a waxy gray and the passage of air through his cracked lips is feeble and ineffective. I reach out and shake him and yell close to his ear, "Breathe, Mr. Easton. Breathe for me."

At the same time I punch in the numbers on the telephone at his bedside to call for the code team with one hand, while I push the button that will lower the head of his bed with the other. While I wait for the code team, I begin what I know will be the unsuccessful process of resuscitating Mr. Easton.

Within minutes the room is crowded with doctors, nurses, and respiratory therapists: pushing, prodding, injecting, intubating, shocking, and shouting.

Mr. Easton dies in spite of our efforts.

In the quiet that descends upon the room as the code team makes their exit, I once again take hold of Mr. Easton's hand as tears fill my eyes.

My Dad's Greatest Gift

Working in a busy emergency room, I deal with death and dying on a regular basis. On this evening of November 11th, I was aware it was my deceased father's birthday and quietly whispered, "Happy birthday, Daddy. I love you." I had lost my father 12 years ago (when he was 57) and remember everything he ever taught me about life and death. Best of all, I never felt he left me at all because he is always in my heart. He is the reason I am who I am and the reason I am able to do what I do.

That evening was no different than any other evening. The ALS radio screamed. I listened closely to hear what was about to arrive. It was a call for a man in respiratory failure, who, according to his family, was to be a full DNR.

His wife and only daughter arrived. Their faces were filled with mental anguish and the fear of death, which I think they knew was inevitable. I went in and introduced myself to them and went to the patient and stroked his forehead. I made a secret sign of the cross on his forehead, with a quick prayer for God's will to be done. I then wet his dry mouth with a washcloth and laid his hands outside the covers to invite touch. As I stroked his hand myself, I noticed his daughter come closer to do the same, with his wife of 57 years standing by her side.

I went to them both and wrapped them up in my arms and reminded them that this is what life is all about…helping each other through to the other side. I whispered to them not to be afraid. I told them he was comfortable and was just going to slip into a twilight sleep when he was ready. I told them they should let him know they will both be okay. I explained that patients often hold on for their family's sake, and that by loving him enough to let him go, they would be giving him the greatest gift of all. I told them they should tell him how much he is loved and remind him that the separation is temporary…that one day they will all be together again.

Suddenly, the patient looked all around at us and smiled and waved, like he had not seen his wife and daughter for a long time. It brought a smile to all of us. I said, "Well, it looks like you have been granted more time." I asked if they wanted a chaplain to come and say prayers with them, and they did. After the prayers were said, I told them I was here for them but was going to let them be alone with him. I gave them big hugs and wished them the very best.

Walking out that night, I thought again about my Dad and said one more Happy Birthday, Daddy! You taught me faith, strength and compassion to last all my life and enough to give freely to everyone I meet.

My Story

An oncology patient who had been extremely ill was hoping he would survive until his daughter's wedding. As the wedding approached, it was evident that he would be in no condition to attend the ceremony.

The nurses, case manager and I decided to bring the wedding to him. The conference room on the oncology unit became a chapel.

We draped the x-ray viewer with white sheets to form a window and mounted a stained glass picture of flowers in the "window". A conference table became an altar with a bible and we obtained a minister to perform the ceremony. White paper from an examining table was used as the runner down the center aisle, and flowers and music were provided.

We dressed Dad in his tux and wheeled him to the door of the chapel just as the bride arrived. Gathering all his strength, he stood and walked his daughter down the aisle.

There was not a dry eye in the entire chapel including those of the attending physician.

After enjoying refreshments, the patient returned to his bed - a very contented man. He quietly passed away a couple of days later.

What a privilege to be part of this bittersweet situation!

Never Mind the Patient

Betsy has been a patient advocate for ten years. She loves her job and does it very well. However, on this particular day she did something unusual. Betsy drinks a lot of water and always has a water bottle close by. However, she does not normally take water with her when she visits a patient.

This particular day, Betsy was called to a floor, usually managed by one of her colleagues, to provide notary services for a patient who wished to complete an advance directive. While in the patient's room, Betsy reached for her water bottle on several occasions, taking large swigs of water. After completing the advance directive she left the patient's room carrying the water bottle. Making stops along the way, Betsy returned to her office several minutes later and, to her surprise, found her water bottle on her desk.

Betsy became hysterical when she realized that she had, in fact, been drinking the patient's water. She immediately contacted her director to report the incident. The director was mortified to learn that Betsy had been drinking the patient's water, and was very concerned from a customer service standpoint that Betsy would have considered taking something to drink into the patient's room in the first place. The whole time Betsy yelled, "Never mind the patient, what about me...do you think the patient could have something contagious? What should I do?"

It was suggested that she contact the patient's nurse to see if there was any need for concern. Betsy tried to contact the nurse, but talked a resident instead. Of course the resident burst out laughing upon hearing the story and asked her if she made a habit of drinking out of patients' water bottles. Betsy was told there was no need to worry, but she continued to be upset and embarrassed about what she had done.

The following day, Betsy reported to work to find a six pack of water on her desk, with her name prominently displayed on each bottle and a little note, which read "be sure to drink only from bottles with your name".

Never Put Off Until Tomorrow

One day, just as I was getting ready to clock out and go to an appointment, I received a call from one of our Social Workers. She and her husband, our patient, needed some documents notarized. I told her I had an appointment after work and didn't think I could help that evening and asked if we could do this the next day. Her voice was hesitant with a hint of desperation to get these documents completed.

I arrived in the patient's room and discovered that there were a number of documents to be notarized. The patient was a pleasant, intelligent man. He joked with me as we notarized the many documents. I was there for over one hour. The man I met was loving and thoughtful. You could tell how much he loved his wife as they interacted with one another.

After completing my notary's duties, I finally left for home. I was exhausted, but had enjoyed meeting this patient. When I returned to work the next day, I asked where my co-worker was because I wanted to tell her how much I enjoyed meeting her husband. I was told that her husband had expired early that morning.

The documents we had notarized were a loving husband's last actions to ensure his wife would be adequately provided for when he was gone. As ill as he must have been, he had garnered his energy to laugh and joke with a stranger. I felt a real loss for all of us in this man's passing. The world, I am sure, suffers in his absence.

Nick & the Veterans Facility

This medical center has different rules and regulations it must abide by because it is a federal installation. We serve a very special group of people, those who have served in the military, and many of whom have been to war. We are currently in wartime.

Several months ago a patient named Nick enrolled in our health care system because he had retired and had no insurance. He lives in a rural community in this state. Due to our long waiting list, the patient was assigned a medicine team, doctor and given an appointment for eight months away. This was fine with him, as he was in good health.

However, a few weeks after he enrolled, he started to feel sick, began to lose weight, and became concerned. He went to the emergency room at a local hospital near his home. They ran tests and determined he had terminal cancer and a bowel obstruction. He needed to have surgery within two weeks.

He came back to our facility's emergency room, telling the nurse what he had been told at the local hospital. She took his vital signs and sent him to the clinic he had originally been assigned to because his need for care was not life threatening at this time.

He was again triaged by the clinic nurse, to whom he had told the same story about his diagnosis and his need for surgery. He was told since he was in no acute distress and had a private physician that he should continue treatment with his doctor in the private sector and return to our facility for his scheduled appointment in eight months.

The patient and his wife returned to their rural community, not knowing what to do now, because they had no insurance and no private doctor, not to mention the fear that accompanies the words surgery and cancer.

Nick's brother-in-law, Jim, called him to find out how the appointment had gone at our facility. When Jim learned that Nick hadn't even seen a doctor, he was not pleased, so he visited our facility the next day on behalf of Nick. He spoke to a staff person in the hallway who knew I was a patient advocate. She brought Jim to meet with me.

We spoke at length about his brother-in- law and sister after which I called Nick and asked him to please return to the hospital. Nick and his wife weren't eager to come in because they had been told to wait until August for his originally scheduled appointment.

I spoke with the assistant head of ambulatory care, explaining that Nick would probably not be alive on his original appointment date, because he needed our help now. I explained that Nick had no insurance, no private doctor, and he was eligible for care in our facility because he served his country and was honorably discharged. I told the doctor that Nick had been diagnosed with terminal cancer, and needed to have surgery within two weeks. The doctor asked me to have the patient here at noon the next day with all medical records, test results and films for an examination.

I called Nick again to tell ask him to come in for this priority appointment - he and his wife agreed to come at noon. Nick was examined, and then sent to general surgery where a surgeon and additional staff examined him and reviewed all the material he had provided. Nick was admitted to the hospital and taken to surgery first thing the following morning for the bowel obstruction. Afterwards, the surgeon apologized to Nick and his wife about his experience and unfortunate outcome, and promised to do everything possible to make his remaining time as comfortable as possible.

Nick lived two more months. His family was given a hospital bed, oxygen, and walker, everything they needed to make his life more comfortable. Nick was thankful to the facility and all our staff for helping him. His family still stops in to thank me for what I did for them and continues to sing the praises of this hospital in their community.

When we can make a difference in someone's life as a patient advocate, our position is rewarding and our passion for fighting the system all seems worthwhile.

Oliver

Patients come in and out of our lives. Some of them we never forget, because in our attempt to touch their life in some way, we find that we ourselves are touched. Oliver is one of those patients.

Oliver didn't stand out in any way...although I have always loved the elderly. As I started talking to him, I realized there was a lot he wanted to say, so I simply let him talk. We shared stories and smiled at each other a lot that first afternoon. When I found out that Oliver had a procedure scheduled the next day, I asked him if I could come back in the morning. Oliver said he'd like that.

As promised, I went back to see Oliver the next morning. When I thought it was time to leave and got up to say goodbye, Oliver called me back. As Oliver struggled to get himself up in his bed, I said, "Oliver, what can I do for you?" Oliver said, "Could you please give me a hug?"

All of the clinicians in our hospital were doing their best to take good care of Oliver, but I will never forget that what Oliver really needed that morning was a hug.

As patient advocates it's important for us to remind the clinicians we work with that the human beings we care for aren't just diagnoses, procedures, or things to check off our to-do list. They are human beings that need our compassion and concern.

In his own way, Oliver reminded me that morning that people may forget what you did...but they will remember how you made them feel.

On Blueberry Hill

One Thursday morning I got a frantic call from a nurse in the medical intensive care unit with a patient's family request. "Daddy is dying and it would mean a lot to him and us if we could have Fats Domino singing "Blueberry Hill" via a tape in his room."

Good grief! Even the music stores are not open this early in our town. As patient advocate, I called around to some friends who are musically inclined, and who suggested I download it from the computer. Not really understanding how to do this, I waited until 9am then called the local bookstore, and told the staff in their music department about my dilemma. Luckily they had just the CD I wanted. They agreed to hold it, in case there was a sudden run on Fats Domino that morning....

I dove into petty cash, jumped into my car and sped off to the bookstore, where I purchased the needed music. On the way back to work, I detoured to my home to pick up my daughter's CD player. Back at work, I put an identifying label on the CD player before rushing up to MICU. Entering the room I found the concerned son holding his father's hand, the comatose patient resting in bed.

I chose the Blueberry Hill selection and turned on the CD player. As the music began playing, I edged out of the room as the tears started flowing down the son's face.

Within a few hours, the patient died. The son kept the Fats Domino CD, with my blessing.

I'll never know what the family's connection was to Blueberry Hill. I also know I will never hear that song again without thinking about that devoted son at the bedside of his dying father.

One Last Gift

A 42 year-old patient was dying. She was an alcoholic with advanced liver disease. The court had taken her three young children from her and placed them in a foster home. She hadn't seen them for several weeks. The nursing shift supervisor called and said the court was going to allow the children to visit their mother that evening. She said the patient was very excited and wanted someone to take her to the hospital gift shop to buy each child a gift.

I went to the patient's room and introduced myself. I told her I would be happy to take her to the gift shop to buy presents for her children. She proudly showed me pictures of her children and talked about how excited she was about the approaching visit. She paused, and with a sigh of regret, told me she had no money to buy the gifts. She asked about borrowing money from the hospital. I helped place her in the wheelchair and told her not to worry about the money. I knew that technically this wasn't a "service recovery" issue but we were going to treat it like one. So I wheeled her, IV and all, to the gift shop.

When we entered the gift shop, she was like a kid in a candy store. She had me push her all around the shop as she carefully selected gifts for her children. She found a beanie baby for her son, a small doll for her youngest child and a necklace for her oldest daughter. She asked if she could pick out a few pieces of candy for them too. I readily agreed. After purchasing the items, I wheeled her back to her room.

As I helped her crawl back in bed, she asked if there was any way we could wrap the gifts. I began an intensive wrapping paper search, finally finding some old, crinkled tissue paper in public relations. I took the paper to her room. She literally clapped her hands with glee when she saw the paper in my possession.

I spent several minutes wrapping the presents with her, listening to her excited chatter about the upcoming visit. She carefully placed the wrapped gifts on her bedside table and eagerly awaited the arrival of her children.

The next morning I stopped by her room to ask about the children's visit. Her eyes literally shone as she talked about her kids. She said they loved their presents and seemed so happy to see her. She talked for a few minutes about how they had grown and how much she missed them. The love for her children was evident by the glow on her face. She thanked me again for taking her to buy the presents.

A week or so later, I stopped in to visit with her again. She didn't remember me and it was quite obvious her condition was rapidly deteriorating. In just a few days she slipped into a coma and within a week she died.

I think about her every now and then and am so thankful I had the opportunity to make a small difference in her life by taking her on her shopping spree. I am certain her children will always treasure the memories of one of their final visits with their mother.

One Smart Dog

I was looking out my office window into the parking lot and saw a large dog jump out of the back of a truck. I quickly went to the front entrance of the hospital, arriving just in time to see the automatic doors open and the dog run straight into the lobby, as though it knew exactly where it was going.

The security personnel saw the dog, too. Patients and staff were treated to a parade of sorts: one dog running, being enthusiastically chased by a patient representative, with security running behind!

Where did the dog go? Right to an exam room door, where it sat down then barked. The physician in the room opened the door; the dog went in and settled down beside the patient.

They let the dog stay in the exam room.

Other Duties as Assigned (How I Became a Clown Mom)

As patient advocates we always get assignments that don't fall easily under any other department. That is how I inherited "Healing Clowns."

I invited the director of nursing, the activity therapist, and managers of the birthing center and the skilled nursing facility to a meeting. Six professionally trained clowns arrived in the boardroom in full nurse or doctor clown attire. Those of us who feared clowns were charmed by the clowns, who could make you smile, open up and share concerns.

We immediately agreed we were convinced we would welcome them on all units except the psychiatric unit. They made our staff smile and gave one dying patient a chance to have a picture with her granddaughter. The granddaughter, a nurse, has that picture as a reminder of how well we cared for her grandmother.

With a $60 Polaroid, $20 of film, business cards and red foam noses, we have opened lines of communication for our patients and staff. I am proud to be the mother of clowns.

Our Grand Reunion

A patient on our transitional care unit contacted me because his glasses were missing. His name sounded familiar because I had a professor by the same name at a small school in Vermont – a school that had closed many years ago when it went bankrupt.

I went up to the patient's room to interview him, and he said I looked familiar. He asked if I had been his student at a local university where he taught. I told him I had never attended that school, but I also questioned whether he had ever been a professor at the small, now defunct college in Vermont.

Incredibly, he confirmed that not only was he a professor of mine, but he had also headed up the office to which I had been assigned as a work-study student when I was a freshman.

We both agreed that this was a remarkable coincidence! We had a grand reunion catching up on the passing years and updating each other on the people with whom we had maintained contact.

As patient advocates, it's amazing whom you can meet. So many years and so many miles from Vermont – we had both relocated to another area. Although we had never run into each other, when the need arose, I was there!! I am still looking for his missing glasses, but at least we found each other.

Outside Friends

I received a call this last year from our chaplain making me aware of a patient/family situation that presented itself. A 65- year-old man was in the cardiac step down unit with his daughter. She was about 30 years old and had not been out of her house for years. The adult protection advocate had slipped notes under her front door each month for years. Now she was here at our facility with her father.

The staff began immediately to try to assist this family. The adult protection advocate was called and she arrived to meet this woman for the first time face to face. The advocate could not have been more helpful. She drove the daughter home every couple of days to take care of her cat, while I stayed with her father while she was gone.

This young woman adjusted remarkably well to her sudden life change. She was friendly and talkative. We never did find out what happened to lead her to the confined life she led, but we were friends to her during this difficult time. Her father was released after several weeks, but returned several months later to expire in the ICU unit. The daughter looked for "her friends" at the hospital when she and her father returned.

I think this experience prepared her for the life she now must lead alone. She made friends here at our facility and hopefully, helped her to understand that in the "outside" world there are also people who wish to help her and be her friend. She sent me a beautiful note sharing her appreciation to "all the angels God sent to help her."

Piano Player

It has been 16 years since I handled a certain situation, however, I don't think I shall ever forget this patient.

I received a call one morning from one of our unit managers asking a favor of me. She said, "Melissa, if anything can be done, I know you are the one who will make it happen." Hesitantly I replied, "OK, so tell me what is on your mind." The manager shared that she has a very good friend, Meg, who had been brought in late last night and delivered a baby boy by emergency C-section.

Kyle came six weeks early and had to be transferred to a Children's medical center. Meg had lost a tremendous amount of blood, was packed during the surgical procedure and admitted to ICU. She was stable at the moment but was losing the battle to live. Family and friends have been asked to do whatever they can to get her "spunk" back. The manager continued to explain that the only picture taken of Kyle before he was transferred was very blurred. She thought if there was some way of getting something of Kyle's to his mom to hold on to, it might give her the will to fight.

Meg was facing a secondary surgery to undo the packing. Her chances of survival were 50/50. Without the "spunk" she normally demonstrated her chances of survival were weakening. What a challenge! I told the manager I would do my best and that I would stay in touch throughout the day.

Whenever I am faced with a situation, I try to put myself in the patient's shoes. My first thought was if I could not hold my baby, then what could I hold of his that was a part of him. I called over to the ICU unit at the Children's Center and requested to speak to the supervisor. When she came on line I introduced myself and explained the nature of my call. (Remember this was long before HIPPA.)

This supervisor was great. She educated me that in these types of situations Children's would make a videotape of the baby with complete dialog of what mom would be seeing. She could have this tape completed within two hours. They would also provide an actual blanket that Kyle had used and a bottle used to feed him. We then scheduled a time that I could pick the items up to bring them back to mom.

I then contacted the unit manager of ICU, explained the request made by Meg's friend, and shared what I had learned from Children's. This manager explained that we would need the approval of Meg's physician to show her the tape, as Meg's condition was very fragile. This manager volunteered to make that contact and suggested that I find a portable TV and VCR. Within an hour the TV and VCR were delivered to the ICU unit.

By early afternoon, I had picked up all of the items from the medical center. Meg's physician had given approval with the caveat that he review the video tape to make sure the information would not upset Meg. Together, the physician, the ICU unit manager, the unit manager who was her friend and I watched the tape.

Children's did a wonderful job on the tape. They began with Kyle sleeping in his basinet and then began at the top of his head going down to all ten toes explaining the necessary IV lines along the way. I remember distinctly when they got to Kyle's hands, because one of the nurses put her finger into his palm stretching out his fingers and said, "Look Meg, little Kyle here has long fingers and he is going to be a great piano player someday." By the time the tape ended, there was not a dry eye in the room. The physician wiped his eyes and said that this was the best medicine anyone could offer Meg.

We sent the friend into the waiting lounge, to explain to Dad and both sets of grandparents what we had done. We asked them if they thought Meg could handle a video of her son. They said yes. We then invited all of them to come to Meg's bedside. We had everything set up and ready to go. As the family entered the room, the physician explained to Meg what they were about to see. All of the staff left the room to provide a private moment as the family gathered near to Meg holding on to each other. We all felt a certain bonding as we could hear Meg and her husband's comments. This moment could not have happened without the team effort of everyone involved

Once the tape was completed the friend gave Meg the blanket that was in the video that was wrapped around Kyle, along with the bottle for her to hold. Meg thanked her friend for making all of the arrangements. The friend then told Meg that she wanted her to meet me as I had made all of this happen. I was brought into the room and introductions were made. Meg and I talked a little about what she had facing her. She said that she now had something to fight for. Meg and I then made a date. I told her that once she and Kyle were both out of the hospital and into a routine, I would like to meet him in person. Meg smiled and shook her head yes.

Three months later, there was some commotion outside of my office area. Another employee who worked in my area came to my office and said that she needed my assistance with a visitor. As I stepped into the hallway there stood Meg holding Kyle. Meg looked at Kyle and said, "I want you to meet a very special lady." She then handed Kyle to me.

As I looked him over, he grabbed my finger and that is when I noticed that Kyle's fingers were long and that someday he would make a great piano player.

Positive Outlook

I'm amazed sometimes at the positive outlook some people have, in spite
of the adversity in their lives. A ninety-ish elderly lady came into the
Emergency Department with some complications. She had several
medical problems, and because she was terminal, was involved with
hospice. It was decided that she should be admitted, but due to high
hospital census, there were no available beds. So she was kept in the ED
for 40 (yes, FORTY!) hours, until an inpatient bed could be found for
her.

Once she was taken to her room and hospice was notified, they came
quickly to her bedside. Worried about the unpleasantness of being kept
in Emergency for so long, they asked her, "Mrs. Smith, how ARE you?
We're so sorry you had to wait so long in the ED!" To which sweet little
Mrs. Smith replied, "Oh no! It was wonderful! Do you know they brought
me PUDDING?! I felt like I was on a cruise!"

Prayers are Answered Every Day at St. Francis

It never ceases to amaze me how God works...

It was my patient's first chemo treatment, and I wanted to do everything possible to make him feel more at ease. I sometimes offer to pray with my patients, but unfortunately I had no opening to do so with this patient.

My heart was broken when he received his first chemo treatment and suffered every reaction in the book. I felt that if I had offered to pray with him, he would not have had such a hard time. I know that we are allowed to pray with patients, but I never offer unless they bring up the subject or mention God in their conversation.
This time, however, I wished that I had mentioned it to him.

Returning for his second chemo treatment, this patient was very nervous and scared because of his earlier experience. Then, before I had a chance to offer to pray with him, he made the request himself. My heart leaped! I prayed with him, and we both cried. After 15 minutes of treatment without any problems, we prayed again. This time I thanked God ahead of time for hearing our prayers and answering them. I praised him for his love. The rest of the treatment went well, and my patient left with confidence that there was hope. Relief was clearly evident on his face.

The patient realized that through prayer his hope came directly from God. The patient had professed his faith, left in prayer, and stated that prayer would continue to be an important part of his life. I couldn't be there with this patient during his next treatment, but when I returned to work I had a message waiting for me.

The patient said he had gone to church on Sunday, and he wanted to thank me, as one of God's "Angels," for reminding him that he had a friend in Jesus, and also reminding him that he had always had this friend.

Pretty Printed Muumuu

My office phone rang. It was a request from a patient's husband, asking me to come and talk with him and his wife. They said they had a problem with the hospital. Yes, this is what I do. So without hesitation I said I would come right up. I hung up the phone and headed to the patient's room.

The hospital was beautiful and only a few months old. It looked like a fine resort somewhere in the woods. Many rooms had beautiful views of the woods, and patients had not even occupied many of the rooms yet. I believe this was my first visit to this particular room. I knocked at the door, introduced myself, and entered the room.

In the corner of the room was an elderly little man, little because his feet appeared to not reach the floor as he sat in the recliner chair. Next to him in the bed was a woman approximately the same age, sitting up in bed wearing a hospital gown. The next thing I noticed was what the man was wearing – it was a multi- colored knit shirt, with horizontal stripes that stretched quite tightly across his large belly, looking much like a shirt two sizes too small. With the shirt, he had chosen to wear a pair of cotton - you guessed it - plaid slacks. Not a subtle plaid, but a quite large, colorful plaid. Maybe it was because he was sitting down that his ankles appeared much sooner than one would expect, but you could not help noticing that his ankles were covered with white athletic socks that were tucked into well-worn, brown leather tie shoes.

I pulled up a chair and said, "How can I help you?" He said we have a problem here. At this point it appeared that he was going to do the initial talking for the patient, so I let him continue. "You see Clara here brought a dress in with her to wear home from the hospital, and you don't have any hanging space in this room for me to hang it up so it won't get wrinkled." "I'm sorry," I said; "let me look in the closet here." "I've already done that and it won't work, the closet is too short." Too short, I thought to myself, how a closet can be too short, when the couple sitting here both look no taller than five feet.

Pushing my chair out of the way, I opened the closet door, and he was right, it 'was' too short. The clothes hanger was placed halfway down the length of the closet and a shelf had been placed above the hanger. "Please let me check another room," I said, "You see this hospital is so new I don't believe I have checked out every patient room yet."

I went to the empty room next door and here was a nice closet, with the hook up high and hangers standing empty, ready for clothing. A nurse saw me in the hall coming out of the empty room and asked what I was doing. I told her about the closet problem and she said, "Oh, I just found out the other day that a few rooms were made handicap accessible and therefore things are placed at a lower level for people in wheel chairs, etc." Well, that answered my question regarding why the low clothes hook.

I reentered the room and explained to the couple why the hooks were placed lower in the closet in their room. At this point, the man stood up. I could not help note that the pants were not just short appearing as he sat in the chair; they were short even as he stood. He went into the bathroom and appeared back in the room proudly holding the brightest, largest flower, polyester muumuu dress I have ever seen. "Now tell, me what are you going to do about this?" as he proudly held the dress up. "We can't keep it hanging in the bathroom, and it will get wrinkled if we put it in the drawer or in the little closet," he said.

I looked at the dress, looked at my little man in the colorful outfit and immediately began to bite my lip, pinch my arm, and anything else I could think of to keep the giggles from coming out. He was so serious. The patient still had not spoken. She just sat in the bed smiling, seeming quite pleased that he cared so much about her and was advocating for her needs.

Well, again, as patient advocates we never know just what we will be faced with when we answer the call to our profession. Sometimes our role is to listen, advocate, and problem solve. I had listened. I now needed to advocate meeting their needs and problem-solve if I could. I asked why we couldn't leave the dress on the bathroom hook until she went home. He didn't like that idea, as staff might knock it on the floor.

It needed to be in a closet. My next choice was to do what I hated to do, I went and found the patient's nurse and said, "Do you have any ideas?" She was so kind; she said without hesitation, "Let's move them into the next room. We have plenty of empty rooms right now, I'll check with the supervisor to make sure it's okay."

We got the move approved. The staff was gracious as they helped change out everything to the room next door. None of us needed to move the dress, the little man, with the round belly, striped shirt, plaid pants, and white socks, proudly held the pretty print dress high in the air, as he carried it to the next room and proudly placed it in the closet. He admired it for a minute and then closed the closet door. The patient smiled, the man said thank you and I thanked the staff. As I walked down the hall, I pictured in my mind the day of the patient's discharge – walking down the hall together, she in her polyester, bright floral print muumuu type dress, and he in his colorful outfit. How did I know they would be so colorful on the day of discharge?

You see, I visited my little couple the next day in their new room, and he proudly said, "We're going go home today!" I wished them well, stepped over to shake his hand and he stood up, smiling from ear to ear, wearing the same plaid pants, a new horizontal multicolored striped shirt, and same well-worn brown leather shoes. He thanked me; the patient then thanked me, and said how very pleased she was that her dress did not get wrinkled. What a kind and sweet couple – how happy they were, and what a delightful mental picture I was left with in my mind, thinking of them hand in hand, walking out the door. Another problem solved!

Problem Daughter

An 89-year-old woman was admitted to the post surgery unit after GI surgery. Her daughter, an only child, moved across the country to be with her mother, as recovery was slow. Her mother's GI tract was not functioning properly and the surgeons thought she was going to live just a short time longer.

The daughter was very nice, but unreasonably demanding. When she did not spend the night, she arrived in the morning and became very vocal whenever anything was not just right with her mother (room too cold, covers off, not bathed yet). She would call me and I would come to the room and listen to her concerns and pass on to the staff.

The daughter's expectations were for the kind of care that her mother would get with constant one-on-one care. We would talk about the situation; the daughter would calm down and feel better. The staff moved the mother to a room right across from the nurse's station, so they could watch her whenever the daughter had to leave.

Days turned to weeks, weeks into months as the patient continued to have highs and lows. The daughter would remove her mother's feeding tube, and then be overcome with guilt and order it put back.

During this time the daughter lost her business (due to her long absence). The nurses continued to deal with the outbursts and demands very well. She did continue to call me, but it became apparent that her respect for our hospital and staff were growing, slowly but growing.

As Christmas rolled near, the nurses got together, purchased and decorated a small Christmas tree for the patient and her daughter. Through the ups and downs, they all grew closer and closer. Until spring rolled around and after months with us, the mother finally expired. Tears rolled as the daughter hugged everyone and even spoke of moving back to her hometown after experiencing this very difficult time.

Real Stories from a Patient Advocate

Too much information: He was a big burly guy and walked in my office and closed the door behind him and said, "I need to show you something". He proceeded to remove his jacket, then his shirt and, fearing what else he might remove, I quickly said, "Oh sir, I am not a medical person and I am not allowed to look at patient's bodies." With that, he put his shirt and jacket back on and sat down and proceeded to describe his complaint about a "rash on my butt that the Emergency Room doctor refused to look at."

A "suit"able injury: A rough looking fellow came into my office and rolled up his sleeve and complained that the lab tech had caused a large bruise on his right forearm. I examined the bruise, apologized but assured him, it was not an unusual occurrence particularly since he is on Coumadin. I suggested he go home and put warm packs on his arm. He said he wanted compensation. I said that was not likely to happen since this was not an intentional injury, but a known complication. He said, "This has really interfered with my sexual functioning and as you know, juries are very sympathetic with situations like mine. Just give me $10,000 and I will release you from all responsibility." While I worked very hard not to even think about how a bruised right forearm interfered with his sexual functioning, I assured him there was no possibility of compensation, and repeated that he should keep his arm elevated with warm packs.

Thou shall not judge: I was called to a patient room because he was "cursing and yelling and threatening to get up and leave." As I got off the elevator, I was met by two nurses who said, "Please, don't talk tattoo man out of leaving AMA." I went to the patient's room and saw a young man who was literally covered with colorful tattoos. He was struggling to put on his pants, while one arm was strapped on an arm board and connected to an IV pump. He was grimacing in pain and cursing loudly.

I asked if I could help him and he said, "Take this ***IV off so I can get out of here. I asked why he was insistent on leaving since it was obvious that he was in a great deal of pain. He responded, "I was in an accident last night and the surgeon they called put me in here. I have been asking for something for pain for the last three hours and they say there is nothing they can do because the doctor is in surgery. I can lay home in pain and at least pop Tylenol."

He was sweating and grimacing and I said, putting my hand on his arm, "Please let me help you get back in bed and give me 15 minutes. Then I promise, I will remove your IV myself and help you get to your car." It was excruciating to watch how he suffered laying back down in his bed. A quick review of his chart and I found out he had two right front rib fractures and two left posterior rib fractures. In other words, there was no possible way this man could lay, stand or sit that wouldn't hurt.

Nursing staff informed me he did not have a primary physician and the surgeon that admitted him from ER was in surgery and could not be disturbed. He had orders for Vicodin from ER, but the surgeon had subsequently put him NPO for possible surgical intervention. I went to the OR and spoke to the nurse manager who agreed to give the surgeon the message that his patient was in severe pain and threatened to leave AMA. I am an RN, and further offered to take his verbal order and carry it out. He shouted out an order for Morphine and I went back to the floor, wrote the order and gave it to the charge nurse, asking her to treat it as a "stat".

Went back to the patient and assured him help was on the way. Trying to keep him distracted a bit I asked what he did for a living and he said, "I'm a tattoo artist. I practice new techniques and colors on myself. My kids call me rainbow dad. Please tell the nurses I'm sorry for how I acted, but I just can't take the pain any more and every time I asked I was told they didn't know how long before the doctor would be out of surgery and order something for pain. I think I could have stood it if they said, a half hour or an hour, but not knowing when I would be able to breathe without pain, that was more than I could take.

He had tears running over two intertwined multicolored serpents on his left cheek when the nurse came in and gave an IV push injection. I watched him relax and finally rest. I went out to the nurses' station to inform the staff that "rainbow dad" is a tattoo artist and is really sorry for his behavior. I also mentioned that fractured ribs all the way around a ribcage were the most unimaginable torture I could think of.

I went back to check on him before going home and he had been put on a PCA pump and was very comfortable. He thanked me for helping him. I thanked staff for taking such good care of him.

Why listening matters: A sweet little lady came to my office and lifted her shirt. There were three oozing angry sores on her shoulders. She said, "I am allergic to Nitropaste. I told the doctor and all the nurses I was allergic to Nitropaste, but they said the doctor ordered it so they had to put it on. I got these sores now and because I'm diabetic, they aren't healing and they just hurt so badly. I wanted you to tell them so this doesn't happen to someone else." I thanked her and apologized and sent her flowers. I have used this story at every new employee orientation for the last five years to illustrate the absolute necessity of listening to our customers.

Friendly Fire: The head nurse listened impatiently to my report and said, "Do you always take the side of the patient?" I reminded her that all of us are "on the side of the patient" because that is our job that many complaints have no basis in fact, but a perceived uncaring attitude is the major underlying component. She replied, "But don't you think these people just complain to avoid paying their bill?" I informed her that a very small fraction of complainants demand write-offs. Most of them just want to be listened to, or to make sure "it doesn't happen again."

In the "Well, Duuuh!" category: A physician who is VERY well acquainted with my complaint response forms was reviewing charts when I entered the room to review a couple of records. He saw me and said, "Well, do you have any questions you want to ask me about?" I replied that I had not had anything with his name on it in a long time and I commended him enthusiastically. He said with such innocence I wanted to hug him, "I'm trying a different approach. I walk into each room and introduce myself and shake the patients' hand. I guess that means something." I praised him and congratulated him on "humanizing the patient and yourself with that small courtesy." "Yeah," he said. "I guess maybe that is what happened."

No dummy here: A secretary from admitting brought a lady to my office and said, "She's a diabetic and she's here to visit a friend and she is having a low blood sugar episode. Can you give her a meal ticket?" This was the third time this had happened so I asked the lady if she had eaten at home. She said, "Yes, but after I get done at the grocery store and then come here, my blood sugar gets low and I need to eat to get back home." I asked if she got low blood sugar at the grocery store and she said, "Well, no. They don't give out meal tickets there."

The rest of the story: I was called to talk to a patient who wouldn't let anybody in her room and kept throwing things at anybody who tried to go in. Fighting off my first response that was "So call a code, and leave me alone!" I went to the room. I opened the door slowly and seeing there was nothing left on the bedside table or stand to throw, I stepped over all the stuff on the floor and got next to her. She was facing the window and said, "Get the hell out of my room."

I pulled up a chair and sat down right next to the bed and told her who I was, and that I was very sorry she was so upset and would she like to talk about it. She said nothing. I started picking up her things and putting them on the bedside stand without a word. I asked her if I could call housekeeping to mop the floor so that she wouldn't fall and get hurt. Then the dam burst. She said, "I wish I would fall, I wish I could jump out the window and die."

I sat down next to her and said, "You wish you could die?" She said, "You would too. I'm 23 years old and I have a 2 year old and a 6 month old and my boyfriend is in jail. Now I am told I had a heart attack and I am diabetic and they put me on a diet and bring me diet pop. I hate diet pop. And your skinny dietitians come in and talk to me about diet when all I can afford and know to make is macaroni and cheese."

I said, "That has to be really scary." She continued crying and talking about what had happened to her. She gave me permission to call Social Services to see what could be done for her. I asked the dietitian if we could give her a little four ounce can of real pop once a day and she said they would work it into her diet if she would discuss diet with them. She agreed. As I was leaving the unit, the charge nurse asked me, "What kind of mo-jo or voodoo do you do?" "I listen. I pretend I have time, and I listen."

No good deed goes unpunished: I had assisted a woman with a lot of problems with her late husband's account. I had found some errors and made some corrections. Then I sent her a letter apologizing for some care issues that I had addressed with the unit manager. I tucked in a $25 gift certificate to our gift shop.

She came in two days later and said, "How dare you insult me by sending me a bribe?" Before I could say a word, she ripped up the gift certificate and threw the pieces at me and left. I picked up the pieces and redeemed them for a new gift certificate. You can't win 'em all.

Reunited

Hazel, a patient in the PCU/CCU was failing. With startling white hair and bright blue vacant eyes, her brain functions were diminishing. The doctor needed a code status, as he believed she did not have long to live. The four adult children refused to have any part of the decision-making, leaving that to Hazel's husband, John. We were told that John was under a protection from abuse order and not allowed to see his wife. I was called to assist.

The doctor revealed the patient had a court appointed guardian who was out of the country. Calls to his office went unanswered. I decided to speak with the estranged husband, who happened to be extremely hard of hearing and had no telephone. I wrote a letter and had it delivered to his home by Dan, one of our security guards. Dan reported back that John seemed lonely and had talked to him for some time. He also indicated that John was open to our visit.

John met with me the next day. Not knowing what to expect, we met on the unit where his wife lay near death, with a security guard nearby. John's tale was one of an annual trip the previous summer with his wife. While they were gone, he said his wife just "lost it and never came back." He said he found her running down a highway, away from him. He got her back into their camper only to have her constantly try to run away, not remembering who he was. He tried to restrain her in the truck by securing the seatbelt, only for her to escape and run to a camp where she told people she was being kidnapped. Again, John got her in the truck; his only thought was to get her safely back to their home in rural Pennsylvania.

The people at the camp called authorities and by the time John and Hazel reached their home, she was picked up by authorities, taken to a nursing home, a court appointed guardian had been named, and John could no longer see his wife. Due to his deafness, he never really knew why. He only knew his wife of over 50 years had been taken from him, he could not see her, and three of his four children would have nothing to do with him. These were the same children who refused to assist the doctor or help make decisions for Hazel as she lay in the hospital.

I arranged with security for John to see his wife for the first time in 10 months. He was allowed to enter the room, see her and talk to her, but not touch her, as we still believed there was a restraining order in effect. Hazel didn't respond to his visit, but the pain in John's eyes, the tears and the gratitude at being able to see his wife spoke volumes.

Further investigation with local court authorities revealed the court order had been for one month and had expired nine months before. It was the result of the children's perception of the trip when Hazel "lost herself." The guardian, still out of the country, was contacted via a resourceful nurse who had a friend who worked in the same city as the guardian's office. This friend delivered a note and taped it on the door of the guardian's law office. His secretary responded to our plea for them to contact our hospital, and discussions began. In the meantime, I allowed observed visits between John and Hazel. He simply sat at his wife's bedside, holding her hand.

The guardian, working with me through his staff, finally allowed John to make decisions for Hazel. John and I talked about her wishes. Even though Hazel had begun to stabilize, John felt that if she were about to die, he did not want life support because he didn't want her to suffer any more. A level 5 DNR was established.

Every day, he sat with his wife, holding her hand and watching over her. I went to see John one day and because of his hearing, he stood up and turned toward me. As he stood, Hazel began to reach out, trying to re-grasp her husband's hand, which he held out to her behind his turned back. He cried and thanked me over and over saying that if it wasn't for me, he might never have seen his wife again, and he would never have known why. Finally, Hazel was well enough to return to the nursing home.

She remained unable to speak, but John visited her nearly every day, to sit and hold her hand.

During those many days of intervention, conferences with court officials, the guardian's office, with doctors and with the help of several staff here, I learned the power of patient advocacy and the importance of teamwork in helping those who come to us in need.

Richard

Richard wasn't expected to live. His nurse, Lisa, went in and out of his room frequently. She was a good nurse. She really cared about her patients and it bothered her that she couldn't spend more time with Richard. She was grateful that he had sons and daughters who made frequent visits. She could tell that they were a loving family.

When Richard died and the family came to thank her for the wonderful care she had provided, she looked at them with surprise. She admitted how she felt…that she hadn't been able to spend enough time with him, because of all the other demands that her job required.

And then the family looked at her with surprise. They reminded her that she always had a smile on her face when she walked into the room and that she always had a friendly comment to try to lift their spirits. They reminded her that she always used their father's name when she spoke to him. They reminded her that she always held his hand for a few seconds when it was time to give him his medication. They reminded her that she always patted him on the shoulder when it was time to change his IV bag.

And then they said, "Didn't you realize how much those things meant to our father and to us?" You made our father and our entire family feels like you really cared about him. We knew if one of us couldn't be there with him, that he would be in good hands. And at that time in our lives, it was very important for us to know that.

Richard's family taught Lisa that you don't have to spend a great deal of time with your patients to show them that you care.

A Reminder:

Studies have shown that the most important factor for determining a patient's level of satisfaction is whether or not they feel the staff cared. An important thing for each of us to remember, the next time we walk into a patient's room.

SHCA Networking Has its Privileges

Recently, a fellow employee was having trouble receiving her medical records from a hospital out of state and called me for advice. She and her physician's office had tried for several months in vain to receive the needed records to clear her for an impending MRI.

I advised her I would make a phone call and see what I could find out. I accessed the hospital's website, and found the number for "Customer Service." I spoke to the customer service coordinator at the hospital, who was not aware of the problem, but quickly apologized, took ownership, and stated she would contact the director of medical records and the patient to rectify the problem immediately.

Throughout the course of the conversation I learned she was a fellow SHCA member and a chapter president. In the six years I have been a member of SHCA, I have always been able to call on other hospitals like this with a certain level of comfort, knowing I may make contact with a fellow SHCA member who is always willing to drop what they are currently doing and help immediately.

So far, I have not been disappointed. SHCA networking has its privileges.

The Call

As a patient advocate, sometimes I find myself becoming a little numb from dealing with lost dentures, wait times, and the usual day to day issues. I keep things around me to remind myself that sometimes we get to be heroes too. One of those items is a letter that never fails to remind me of how we touch lives. It was written to our COO, a big burly bear of a man, who scribbled a note to me on it – "this letter really grabbed my heart."

"On Monday afternoon, my mother was brought to your hospital's Emergency Department. I understand she was cyanotic and apneic. Your staff quickly revived her and began a series of tests to determine the cause of her sudden illness. I talked with two people during this initial episode and although I cannot recall their names, I would like you to know that they were informative, helpful and calm.

About an hour later, I called to see if a definitive diagnosis and plan of action had been determined. I was put through to a nurse named Donna. Donna quickly gave me an update and was very reassuring. She then did something I will never forget. She said, 'your mother looks much better now. Would you feel better if you talked to her? This will take a few minutes, but let me bring the stretcher over to the nursing station so she can talk to you.' In a few minutes, my mother and I were chatting away. We laughed about her sudden illness and she assured me that she was feeling much better now. We concluded our conversation with a quick exchange of 'I love you.'

I know Donna was very busy, and I will never forget this extraordinary kindness. You see, the rest of the story is that my mother died suddenly a few minutes after I talked to her. Donna continued to keep me informed by phone of Mom's sudden demise, code status and outcome. She advocated for an autopsy and gently cared for my mother in her final hour.

I am very grateful for the care all the staff provided my mother, and I will never forget the very special nurse named Donna."

It's been four years since that letter came into my life. I still can't read it without tears.

The De-escalator

I received a page from one of our nurse managers who said she needed
for me to come down to the unit immediately to handle an out-of-control
family. She said that the family had been angry, critical and difficult in
their interactions with staff and everyone was on edge. Family members
had been gathering and now there were 10 of them present. The
psychiatric nurse liaison had just spent an hour with them but that had
not settled things down.

I went down and was met by the surgical nurse practitioner that said that
she had never encountered a family like this before. We were joined by the
psychiatric nurse liaison, a 20-year seasoned clinician, who echoed those
sentiments.

I first met with the clinicians involved: surgical attending and nurse
practitioner, pain service attending and fellow, nurse manager, nurse,
social worker, psychiatric nurse liaison. The surgeon said that the
problems had in fact started prior to admission when the family had
contacted the operating room scheduling office to try to bypass his office
to select a time for the surgery, and that the current issues seemed like a
continuation of this pattern.

As I listened and asked questions it seemed that there were two separate
issues. The first was the clinical picture. The patient was four days post
surgery and was having severe pain that had not yet responded to multiple
interventions on the part of the pain service. The second issue was a
cluster of quality of care issues including the fact that the patient had not
been on fall precautions and had attempted to get out of bed, fallen and
hit his head (thankfully without injury).

I recommended a meeting with the key clinicians and representatives
from the family. I facilitated the meeting and began by identifying the
issues and saying that I'd like to focus on the immediate management
issues and that I would separately address the quality of care issues in my
role as patient relations representative.

The meeting began with family locked in to their angry, accusative stance, but as it became clear that staff were very concerned about successfully managing the patient's pain, things began to settle down. In the end we had an articulated care plan, an identified "chief communicator" who would speak with the patient's wife at least daily around the overall care, and a designated contact from the pain service. Both family members and staff came to me following the meeting to thank me for de- escalating the situation that had previously felt out of hand, and getting things back on track.

The Lesson

Recently on my rounds I reached across the side rail to grasp the hand of an elderly gentleman whose smiling face and sparkling eyes belied the 95 years the census report said he had accrued. When I questioned him about his care his glance strayed off to the side ever so slightly and a shadow dimmed his smile as he said, "Oh, pretty good."

Unconvinced by his tone I pursued the question and he returned his gaze to mine, this time with a trace of sadness as he said, "They don't listen to me. They think because I'm 95 that I don't know anything."

I heard an echo as my mind flashed instantly to the face of a daughter of a patient who only a few days before had looked deep into my eyes as she tilted her head to gently ask, "Why didn't they listen to me?" I could still hear the confusion and the hurt. Simultaneously, swimming before my eyes, was a line from a survey, the anger apparent in the scrawl of the letters: "They don't listen to you!"

Suddenly, I realized the engaging smile had returned to the face of this gentle man, and he had gone on to tell a story - a story of the time he told two nurses' aides that what they were doing in caring for him was extremely important. In response to their quizzical looks he emphasized, "Oh, it's not me that says that.
It's in the Bible: "What you do to the least of my brethren you do unto me."

I squeezed his hand as he taught me once more the true worth of the hours we spend here in this hospital. I took a deep breath as I turned from his bedside and swallowed hard, marveling once again at the never-ending array of disguises that God will use. I did not know where or when I would encounter Him again, but I did know that it would behoove me to listen...closely.

The Protest

I had just returned to my office after my one-on-one meeting with our hospital's CEO/VP, when I heard a knock on my office door. It was my CEO/VP stating, "We have a picketer in front of the hospital. I sent security out there." I responded, "Great, what a wonderful way to start a Monday morning. I will go out and see if I can talk to the man to see what his issues are and find out if he wants to come in and talk to us." I can honestly say that I did not have a clue what I was going to do. As I started my walk past the parking area toward the street entrance, our medical director was just leaving the building and asked what mission I was on. I told him about our 'friendly picketer,' and he said, "What's his issue?" I told him I did not know, and I was on my way to find out.

I arrived at the street entrance where cars were backed up from coming in and leaving the hospital. Our picketer was very slowly walking back and forth carrying a very large sign that said something about "negligent hospital care at this hospital" on one side and "dollar signs and words about the overcharging of patients" on the other side. Lovely, I thought to myself. The security guard approached me and said he had called the local police. I said, "Is he saying what the issues are?" The security guard said, "He won't talk about it."

He was right! I tried talking to him, walking alongside him as he proudly carried his picket sign in one hand and a cup of coffee in the other. He stated, "I plead the first amendment, and I do not have to speak to you. I have the right to be here!" He kept repeating this phrase to me as he walked. I soon fell out of line and stood to the side.

The hospital medical director had pulled his vehicle off to the side and took my place, walking alongside our unshaven, stocking hat, tennis shoe and shorts-wearing picket sign man. He received the same comments from our picketer and was soon standing next to the security guard and me. I thanked him for trying. He went off to his office to see patients, and I left the security guard at the entrance to wait for the police. I told the guard that he did have the right to picket but added that we would be very appreciative if we could get our new friend to move to the other side of the street. That way he would be on a sidewalk and wouldn't interfere with the traffic flow when the police arrived. I returned to the hospital.

My goal was to find out anything about a patient who might have been at our hospital recently and left upset. I lucked out! I discovered that a patient had left AMA on Friday. The nursing supervisor had spent time with him and was currently writing a report. After getting the man's name, I found out that he had called and left a voice mail message at my work number on Saturday. I then checked back with our CEO, who was also trying to identify our picketer and figure out what we should do next. He was hoping to do something before the whole event ended up on the 5, 6, and 10:00 news! (It was getting close to election time, and healthcare issues were on the news frequently.)

I headed back to the street. (Good thing I chose comfortable shoes that day!) Our picketer friend had moved across the street and all was quiet as he continued his march back and forth. I caught up with him, said his name, and then said, "Hey, you called me. I am the one you wanted to talk to." He stopped walking. I listened, and listened, and listened as we stood on the sidewalk. His picket sign remained in full view of all the staff, the patients, and the visitors. A hospital chaplain drove by and decided it looked like I needed prayer, and indeed I did.

I finally got our picketer to agree to come back to the hospital at another time. I told him I would get a meeting together of administrative staff and hospital staff just to sit and hear his story. He said, "OK," but said he'd like something in writing from me that stated he had permission to be on our property – that we would not call the police or kick him off the hospital grounds. I said I would type something up and bring it right back to him. He said he would finish his picketing in about 15 minutes, after he finished his coffee. Boy, was I happy I hadn't brought him another cup of coffee!

I typed up the permission he requested and headed to administration. As I entered our CEO/VP's office, I noted a room full of people. He looked up and said, "We are trying to plan what to do next." I filled the group in on the agreement I had struck with our picketer. A thankful sigh filled the room.

When I arrived back on the street, our picketer had put the sign in his backseat and was sitting in his car. He had to open his car door to get my letter, as his window didn't work. For the first time, I was a little leery being out there alone with him, but I handed him the letter and thanked him for talking to me. I assured him that we would meet with him soon.

We never know what a 'day will bring' when we start out as a patient and family advocate or representative. During our meeting with Mr. 'Picketer,' he stated to our CEO/VP that he had planned to picket all week long and maybe the next week, too.

However, he agreed to meet with us instead because he thought the patient representative was genuine and sincere.

This Monday morning, as I stood out in the cold wind for almost an hour, I was probably a little kinder and a little more caring than I might have been on another day. You see, the day before, a bright, sunny Sunday afternoon, I said goodbye to my best friend. She lost her battle in a long, courageous fight with breast cancer. I had spent a lot of time walking beside her during many of her treatments and tests and had shed many tears with her.

My job is to care about others, and that is just what I did that early Monday morning. I am a patient advocate because I care not just about my friends, but also about those who look like they may not have any friends.

The Ring Story

A same day surgery patient was scheduled for an elective procedure and was bumped several times due to emergencies. Finally, at 10:00 pm she was taken into OR and was eventually discharged at 2:00 in the morning. The next day her son called Patient Relations requesting assistance in locating his mother's gold 1938 school of nursing ring.

Upon investigation I learned that at our urging, the son had gone to dinner when the patient was called to the OR. Therefore, the nurse placed the ring in a labeled bag with the patient's belongings. When I interviewed the nurse she developed a look of horror as she realized after dressing the patient to go home she must have thrown away the ring with what she thought was an empty belongings bag.

As Patient Advocate, I persevered to the Plant Engineering Department to learn far more than I ever wanted to know about hospital trash. I learned that the dumpster has a compactor feature and that if the ring was indeed there it was now smashed somewhere in the mass of trash. I was also told that under no circumstances could anyone get into the dumpster to search for a needle in a hay stack.

As the nurse felt confident that she had thrown away the ring, I then made a visit to the Director of Surgical Services, Michael. Without hesitation he stated we must find this ring. Six days later the dumpster was transported to the local landfill with our Director of Surgery following behind. Being the gentleman he is, he left without me on his quest. After watching a week's worth of hospital trash being dumped he then proceeded to spend the next four hours on a treasure hunt for the ring.

The next time I saw Michael, he was standing in my doorway, somewhat gamy with hair standing on end, smiling. In his hand was the now famous labeled bag with the unharmed ring! Being the humble soul that he is, he declined to call the patient stating, "the important thing is we found it."

I then called the patient who immediately began to cry sobbing, "You'll never know that this means to me; I can't believe someone would go to that extreme." She then put her son on the phone who said, "I can't thank you enough; my dad is now deceased but many years ago he and my mom had financial problems and they had to sell and hock everything...my mother even sold her wedding ring but she would not sell this one...it is the only thing she has left."

Needless to say we learned that lost belongings are not just lost belongings and that all patients come to us with very important histories and stories.

The Room

They were in their 80's and he had been in the hospital for several weeks. He was in a semi-private room and had shared it with roommates on and off over the length of his visit. His wife could usually be found at his bedside.

There were some maintenance issues with the room and he was moved to a private room across the hall, near the nursing station. His wife was quite upset about the transfer so I was asked to visit with her.

I walked in his room, introduced myself to him and his wife, and before I could say anything else, his wife asked me to please step outside the room with her. She asked me to walk across the hall to his old room and visit with her in there. I readily agreed and so we went to his old room.

I told her how sorry I was about the transfer and began to explain why we moved her husband to a different room. I could easily tell she had heard it all before. She looked me in the eye and emphatically told me she wanted her husband back in his old room. I couldn't figure out why this was so important to her, especially since he had been transferred from a semi-private room to a private room. I was clearly puzzled, so I began to question her about it.

She leaned back in her chair and said, "Let me tell you something." She began to reminisce about when she was a young 18-year-old girl. She said she loved to dance and frequently went to supper clubs just to dance. One night, while dancing, a handsome soldier walked in the room. All evening long, every time she would look at him, he would be watching her dance. She said when other soldiers would offer her cigarettes or beer, she would look at him and he would gently shake his head "no." She told me that later on he asked her out.

She went on a date with him and on their first date, he told her he wanted to marry her. She told him she couldn't marry him because she hardly knew him and besides, they had nothing in common. She told him she loved to dance and he didn't even dance! However, he was hard to resist and in just a few short months, they were married.

She went on to say that when he took her home to meet his parents, his mother told her she had "something" to be passed on to her when she died. She never said what it was and never mentioned it again.

After 12 years of marriage, her husband's mother died. They traveled back to his hometown for the funeral. When they arrived, his father met them at the door and told her he had something for her. He said before his wife died, she told him to be sure to pass this on to her. He handed her a box tied with a yellow ribbon.

She slowly untied the ribbon and took the lid off of the box. The box was filled with letters. She opened the letter on top of the pile. It read, "Mom, I have met the girl of my dreams. I don't know her name, but it is love at first sight. I am going to marry her." The next letter said, "Mom, I know her name now. It is Anne. She is beautiful." And finally, the last letter said, "Mom, sell my chemistry set. I am going to buy her an engagement ring."

She continued to talk about the great love they had experienced through the years. She told me about the decades of happy memories she shared with her husband. She let me know that just a few weeks ago her son and daughter came together to visit their father. She said, "We all sat in this room and laughed and talked and had a wonderful time." She told me it was a precious memory for her. She said, "My husband is dying. This is the room with the good memories. I want him to die here."

With tears in her eyes, she looked at me and said, "After all I've told you, do you think I care about the maintenance problems?" I promised her we would do whatever it took to get the room ready for his return. In less than 30 minutes, there were four employees in the room, diligently working to get the room in order.

A few weeks later, with his wife at his bedside, he passed away. He died in the room with the "good memories."

The Watchmaker

Bob and Jean were one of those awesome couples whose romance still
sparkled after five decades of marriage. They were two of the first
patients I helped when I became a patient rep.
Over the years and our many contacts, we became dear friends.

Bob had numerous health problems that necessitated frequent visits to
our medical group. Jean was always with him. While they waited together,
they always held hands. When Bob was in with his doctor Jean read one
of the thick books she carried with her.

Over the years, Jean and I shared many conversations about our love for
our husbands and the joys of reading. They also became "groupies" at the
semi-annual stress management classes that I taught. Once when Jean
called to confirm their attendance she tearfully told me that Bob's cancer
had returned and the prognosis looked very bleak. "We're hoping that
your class will give us some good pointers to help us through the difficult
days ahead."

That Saturday morning class was one of the most difficult I ever taught.
There they sat front and center, looking at me with hopeful smiles, and
holding hands. As I looked at their bright faces and tightly clasped hands
I have never felt so inadequate. My throat choked and my heart broke.

Shortly before their 50th Anniversary, Bob's condition worsened and he
was placed in a convalescent hospital to wait for the end. In a cruel twist
of fate, his ever-faithful companion was hospitalized with a rare disease
and was fighting for her life.
Bob's final journey was fast - Jean's recovery painfully slow. She didn't
even get to tell her beloved good-bye.

I had been spending many of my breaks at Jean's bedside. Even though
she begged and pleaded to attend Bob's funeral, her condition was too
fragile to even attend on a gurney, or in a wheelchair. I held her as she
sobbed.

The day of Bob's funeral I went to the hospital and stayed with Jean
while her family and friends attended the services. She spent the hours
alternating between reminiscing and crying. When her family arrived at
the hospital, I hugged Jean good-bye and said that I would see her in a
week when I returned from vacation.

The next day we left for our trip – my heart both relishing the time with my husband and breaking for Jean. We were strolling through a resort town gift shop when an angel figurine caught my attention – an elderly male angel sitting on a park bench. He wore a white shirt and a blue bow tie. He had the most gorgeous detailed wings draped over the back of the park bench and held a pocket watch with a small gold chain in one hand. Something about the angel strongly reminded me of Bob, and on impulse I bought it for Jean. The first thing I did when we got home was rush to the hospital to check on Jean and give her the angel that I was already calling Bob.

She held the angel like a treasure and her eyes filled with tears. She looked at the steel gray hair, the slender face and wire- rimmed glasses both on the angel and reflected in the photo of Bob that was beside her bed. Eventually, she noticed the watch. She cried, laughed and looked totally awestruck. "You never knew, but Bob was a watchmaker for 40 years!"

Seems some things are just meant to be.

They Call Us the Angel Team

As the newest member of guest relations, I was a proud, new patient advocate – a position I had coveted for several years. I was on cloud nine. However, reality struck in the form of a co- worker when she humbly told me, "We are known as The Angel Team."

The Angel Team? They had to be kidding! My irreverent humor doesn't quite fit the halo and wings persona. On my best days, my thoughts fall far short of angelic. As patient concerns seemed to become more difficult by the day, I started to doubt my ability to live up to the expectations of the position. How could any human follow through on all the issues presented? Sometimes the concerns are massive and unfixable.

Then, I met Tony. He was a frequent flier and the "bad boy" of the pulmonary unit. The nicest thing I had heard about him was he was "non-compliant." A twenty-something young man who had grown up knowing he would die young, Tony seemed to have a wish to hasten death. The first time I saw him, he was yelling at his physician for more pain medication. The next time, I suspected him of attempting to set up a porn site for the home page of the patient/family use computer on the unit.

Nevertheless, Tony and I talked. He told me about his new motorcycle. (Riding a chopper on heavy doses of pain meds?) He shared his excitement of moving to a new home. We developed a superficial relationship and I no longer dreaded going into his room.

Tony has an older brother who shares the same horrific disease, and is nearer to end stage. One day, his brother developed a crisis. The already-broken family was in a shambles, with shouting matches about the level of care to be given and who was responsible for making decisions, while Tony stood aside and watched. Somewhere in the middle of this, Tony ended up in my arms. He clung to me as he cried for his brother and for himself.

I learned sometimes the most important part of the job is to care. Maybe I can sprout wings...

Tintinnabulation of Infernal Bells

As we know, each medical facility has its own assigned Tooth Fairy. Dentures and partials just vanish – there one minute. Blink. Surprise, Surprise!! They're gone!! If you listen oh so very closely, and tilt your head just right, you can almost hear the maniacal tintinnabulation of the Tooth Fairy's giggling – like tiny, tarnished bells, smashing into each other, grinding and grating.

One morning a patient's wife and daughter came to see me, very distressed. They said that when they left last night, the patient's dentures were safely cleaned and in our bright pink denture cup. Today when they came in, the dentures were missing—just an empty cup and what was the hospital going to do about it, after all it's almost lunchtime!

Sure that the tooth fairy, the little hussy, was working overtime, I called out the troops and began the search. Call the Laundry! Check the trash! Check the bed linens! Scour the room! Paw through every possession the unfortunate patient brought with him! And of course, last but not least, fill out the reports!!

Dismal failure! Our brave searchers could not find the dentures.

An hour or so after lunchtime, the patient's wife called me. She sounded oddly happy and somewhat strained at the same time. I anticipated the reason for her call, and apologized that we were unable to locate her husband's teeth. She surprised me by saying that everything was now OK. She went on to explain that she and her daughter had found the teeth, in the last place they thought to look. Intensely curious, I had to ask, "Where were they?" Very softly, in a small voice, the wife replied, "In his mouth!"

And softly in the distance, I thought I heard the vile grating of those darned bells….

To Share or Not to Share

Life experiences help in our role as patient advocates. I believe the job would be especially difficult without ever personally staying or having a family member stay in the hospital. This was never truer than the day I was called to our cancer center to talk with a patient and his wife regarding their physician.

It is not unusual for me to be called to talk with patients about their physicians, but it always concerned me when it involved this particular physician. He had been my husband's oncologist when I lost him to leukemia two years earlier. I respected the physician very much and knew him to be a very straight forward, no nonsense kind of man.

For us this had been a comfort. We wanted the truth and from the day of diagnosis to the day of death he had been there for us with all the help he could give and all the facts we could handle. That was not always true for other patients.

I went to the cancer center that morning, notebook in hand, to talk with Mr. and Mrs. Smith. I came into the treatment room where Mr. Smith was having chemotherapy and Mrs. Smith was sitting next to him trying to read a magazine. I could feel the fear and grief that filled the room.

I introduced myself, explained my position, and asked them to explain their concerns with the physician. "The doctor wants me to register with hospice," said Mr. Smith. "He is giving up on me and I am not ready to die!" Mrs. Smith added that the physician had said the chemotherapy was not working and that it was foolish to continue with this treatment. Her eyes filled with tears. My heart almost broke.

Mr. Smith had acute myelocytic leukemia (AML), which is exactly what my husband had been diagnosed with. The credo for patient advocacy is to listen and not tell your story. But at that point, I had to make a decision. I could share my story and help this couple through this very difficult time, or I could just listen. I decided that sharing was the right thing to do.

I told them I understood what they were going through, because two years earlier my husband had died from complications of

AML. The look in their eyes was unmistakable—here is someone who understands! They had many questions, including "What was it like at the end?" I explained Jim's death. "Was he in pain?" asked Mr. Smith. I could honestly answer, "No, he just went to sleep."

It was like a weight had been lifted off both of them. Then Mrs. Smith asked me how I was doing. I told them it wasn't easy, but my life has gone on. I also let them know that my children, my friends and my job have helped me get through the difficult times. As I talked, Mrs. Smith seemed to gain some hope that a wife can survive this and so can a family.

I was with them for over an hour, and we agreed that I would call the hospice program and have the nurse contact them for a consultation. It didn't mean we were giving up. We were just looking into the options.

About a month later, I received a call from Mrs. Smith. Her husband had passed away very peacefully at home with his family surrounding him. She called to thank me for sharing my story. It allowed them to accept what was going to happen. Mrs. Smith said her husband had told her that after meeting me and seeing that I was functioning in a normal way, he was convinced that she could too. He also gave up the fear that he was going to be in pain. She said I gave her the confidence to go on, and that their last few weeks together had been easier for them because of their conversation with me.

On days when this job is so difficult and I cannot listen to one more complaint or one more incident where we as an institution have failed to meet the needs of a patient or family, I think about the Smiths and feel good knowing that I made a difference.

Trying to Cover Everything

I received a telephone call from the Minister's office of Health and Wellness for a Canadian province. The caller stated that they had received a couriered package in the mail with a bath towel in it. Included in the package was a complaint letter from a former patient at a local hospital.

The unidentified complainant said that he was "...disgusted with the quality of the towel – it was much too small; it was harsh on his skin; and it wasn't very white." Stating further that, "surely the hospital could get more monies from the government to pay for new and larger bath towels that would cover more of you?" And, he suggested they use something in the rinse water to soften them.

Because of the Health & Privacy of Information Act the sender wasn't identified to me but the Minister's office was forwarding the towel and a copy of their reply to the complainant suggesting he should call me. Nothing was said however about the towel being away from the hospital without permission! I'm still waiting for the call.

Because our cancer treatment center doesn't have in-patients, I'm not sure where the towel came from and, oh yes, the rough, tiny and soiled towel is still AWOL.

Unexpected Inspiration

As patient advocates, we are dedicated to serving our patients, families, visitors, co-workers, and our communities. We give without expecting praise or recognition. We practice servant leadership from the heart. However, life has a way of teaching lessons in the most unexpected ways.

Recently I was listening to the morning radio news, and I heard a tragic story about three college aged students that died in a horrific auto accident very close to my house that was caused by a drunk driver. As they spoke each of the students' names, I realized that I knew one of them. My son had been in day care with her mother for several years. The daughter's sunny smiling face was a constant in their house.

Not only did I know them from day care, but also the mother had returned to work at our hospital when the children were older. I had seen her children at our functions and picnics. It was such a shock to hear that such a wonderful, sweet young woman had met with such a tragic end.

That day, after listening to the morning news, I went to work with a heavy heart. I kept thinking about how sad and unfair this loss was. As my day went on, I received a call from laundry; they had found a rosary. When I went to pick it up, it was in a small plastic bag with a patient name on it. . .her name.

I took it back to my office and agonized about calling her mother. When I placed the call, I apologized for calling during this difficult time, but I explained that I wanted her to know that we had her daughter's rosary. She came in immediately to pick it up.

As she walked in my office, there were not enough words to express my sympathy and condolences to her and her family. However, she assured me that her daughter had VERY strong faith, and she was in a better place. She was not angry or bitter. . .she had a beautiful peace and serenity about her. She was very grateful for the rosary, because it was a symbol of her daughter's love and faith. She told me that her daughter was in heaven.

I was deeply touched by such great faith, a faith that I felt far exceeded my own. I was touched by the hope and lack of bitterness. Amazingly, she even tried later to help the driver of the accident.

In the hospital, I'm reminded on a daily basis of my blessings, simple blessings of health, sight, family and friends. That day I also learned that our patients and families could teach us great lessons of love and faith. I'm striving to be a better, more forgiving soul after her inspiring example.

Vacation Plan

A young lady from out of state came to visit her family and then planned to leave for a week of fun on the west coast.

Unfortunately things didn't go according to her plans and she found herself recovering from emergency surgery. One of the RNs taking care of this patient told her co-workers how sorry she felt for this young lady and they came up with THE PLAN and decided to bring the fun to the patient.

The nursing supervisor facilitated the arrival of some plastic animals and a bucket of Lego's. These were vital components of THE PLAN. One of the LPNs stayed over on her own time to work on decorations. A phone call to another LPN was made to get her permission to transport some decorations that she and her husband had provided on another unit in the hospital.

The next day the RN, nurse tech, and the charge nurse, went to the patient's room and announced to her that she was "going on a trip." They carefully helped her into the wheelchair and off they went to the surgery waiting room. They provided the young lady with coupons that were good for visits to three "vacation attractions."

The young patient used coupon number one to visit the fish tank that had miraculously turned into a famous marine attraction.

Next, everyone followed the signs to the zoo and found him or herself down a hallway where animals of all shapes and sizes were present and even lurking under a large potted plant. While the young patient was gone from her room, two LPNs borrowed a palm tree (with a lighted trunk), beach chairs and a wicker table to give her room a beach atmosphere.

Imagine the patient's surprise when they wheeled her into her room and found not only the beach, but also the famous beach spelled out in Lego's, as well as her name, with a variety of other handcrafted items.

Photographs were taken at each stop. She surrendered her coupons, the young patient could take her photos home along with the zoo animals and Lego's. The palm tree, table and chairs were returned and the staff on the surgery floor gets to keep the wonderful memory of the big smile on the face of a delighted patient.

Wal-Mart

While making patient rounds one day, I stopped in an elderly lady's room. We chatted for a couple of minutes and then I asked her the all-important question. Are you satisfied with your care? She quickly replied, "Oh, yes! It has been wonderful. Everyone is so kind and helpful. They always go out of their way to help me whenever I need it." I felt a surge of pride for our organization as she continued to sing our praises.

I realized she might not be the best testimonial for our facility when she grabbed my hand and said, "But that's why I am here at Wal-Mart. They always give me good service!"

We Did It for the Patient

Just when I thought I heard or been asked to do it all, *it* just keeps outdoing itself.

I received a call from a nurse who had a patient with multiple medical problems, mostly upper respiratory complications. At the present time she was being treated for the condition that causes a persons tongue to swell several times its original size hanging out of the mouth. Jane was in her early 70's and although she was ambulatory her condition was very unstable. She had been a patient for nearly six weeks.

The nurse continued to explain the family had notified Jane's physician and shared some sad news with him; Jane's husband of 56 years had suffered a massive heart attack and died at home the previous day. The family needed to ask Jane how she wanted to handle the funeral arrangements. A family meeting with Jane was scheduled this morning.

As I sat listening I could not figure out why the nurse had called me. I politely asked why she was sharing all of this information with me. The nurse stated that Jane wanted to attend his funeral. But she was not stable enough to leave the hospital, only to the floor.

The nurse continued the physician had called the funeral director to discuss how this could occur. The funeral director indicated they could bring the funeral to the patient if the hospital had a representative they could work with to find the appropriate room to set up.

Once I caught my breath and picked myself up from the floor and in the most professional, courteous and polite voice I could muster, I said, "You expect me to assist a funeral director conduct a funeral on campus?"

"P l e a s e !" was the nurse's response. I needed to get some kind of approval before anything could go forward.

Just as I was collecting my thoughts, my telephone rang. You guessed it - it was the funeral director. Before the conversation was over, I had learned way too much about coffins: how long and wide they are, you cannot bend a coffin or stand it up on end (especially with a body inside). I learned you should not wheel a coffin down a hallway or use a main elevator, as it is not good publicity for a hospital.

All I had to do was find a nice quiet room to accommodate the coffin, stands for flowers, special lights and several rows of chairs for the family and guests. The funeral director would supply everything else needed to make this occasion meaningful. Oh, by the way, if the temperature could be at a certain degree that would be nice too. Easy for him to say!

This situation was a bit over my head, so I needed to get senior management's approval. I called the President's office only to learn that all of our senior management was off campus having a two-day retreat. I then decided this was important enough to page the senior manager on call. It happened to be our chief finance officer who was very gung ho regarding patient satisfaction.

As I shared the story with George, I thought I heard the telephone drop. There was a very long pause and I was beginning to think that our connection had disconnected. George was taking a moment to absorb what I was requesting. The first words that came back across the line to me were, "A funeral?" "Yes," I replied. "A funeral?" he asked again.

"Yes, and they want to have it tomorrow, Friday the 13th." After another brief moment of silence, George said, "Who is going to be in charge?" It was now my turn, "Who do you want to handle this?" Then George surprised me by saying, "You are the only one I trust to pull this off. Please try your best to keep it low key. Let's do this for the patient."

Not exactly the answer I was expecting or hoping for, but it brought a smile to my face. I am always up for a good challenge and I had never had a challenge such as this before. George asked me when the funeral would take place and that would be the exact moment he would tell the rest of senior management the hospital is holding its first funeral. I thanked him for his trust and support.

I notified the nurse the funeral was on. The nurse agreed to handle everything needed to get Jane to the chosen place. With information I had from the funeral director, my first visit was to the maintenance department to borrow a tape measure. I began my journey by contacting Margie, our education coordinator.

Together we looked at the schedule for potential rooms. With tape measure in hand, we both took off to see what would work. It's amazing how short elevators are, and how narrow hallway corners are. We finally found a room to accommodate Jane's husband. The only problem....

George had mentioned I was to try to keep this funeral low key. The room was located in a building directly across the street from the hospital. The only door wide enough to get the coffin through was the front main door of this building. Once you enter the building the room is immediately to the right. However, just past the room is the gymnasium. This gym is utilized for the hospital's blood drives. It just so happened we were in the midst of a two-day blood drive. OK, time to back up and punt!

I called the funeral director and told him everything that had transpired since our first conversation. I asked his advice since he was the professional in this field. He then began to ask me a few questions. Once he heard the responses he devised a way we could conduct the funeral. We shared his plan down to the minute of arrival of Jane's husband. The funeral was back on.

Margie assisted me with getting the room prepared. Our housekeeping department did a magnificent job thoroughly cleaning the room. They actually scrubbed the walls and carpet. They sent the curtains to local cleaners who, after learning what we were trying to do, donated their services.

At precisely 9:30 a.m. on Friday the 13th, the room was set up exactly as if you were walking into the funeral parlor. The hearse arrived at the front door and within a matter of minutes Jane's husband was wheeled into the room. The hearse was moved behind the building so as not to bring attention to the public. The nurse along with a respiratory therapist accompanied Jane. The family and friends began to arrive as we placed them in a gathering area around the corner. At 10 a.m. the funeral services began. We were able to provide Jane a chance to be with her husband and say good-bye.

The only way Jane could communicate was to write on a tablet of paper. She had written a note to the nurse asking who had made all of this happen. The nurse came outside of the room and asked that I step in. The nurse took me over to Jane and introduced me. Jane smiled at me then began to write a message. She wrote, "Are you the one who did this for me?" "It took a group of us to do this for you and your family and it was our honor to do so." Jane then looked at me with tears in her eyes, and patted my hand. I squeezed her hand in return and began to walk away, but Jane was writing something else.

This time when I read the message a very large lump gathered in my throat. In very large letters that covered the entire page, Jane wrote, "THANK YOU." I still have that sheet of paper today, ten years later.

Once the funeral was finished and everyone was gone, the hallway was very silent. At first I thought it was eerie until I soon learned that those donating blood figured out what was transpiring in the room on the ground floor. The hallway was silent due to the respect demonstrated by our employees towards the family members. At that moment, I realized that we had done something very special. We did it for the patient.

The following Monday, I received a call to report to the President's office. He asked me to fill him in on the details of the funeral. He then handed me some letters that had been slid under his door over the weekend. He asked me to take a moment to read these letters.

The letters were from employees who had been donating blood at the time of the funeral. They wanted him to know how meaningful the service must have meant to the family and how proud they were to work for such a fine organization. He then asked me why I went out on the limb to do this. I looked at him and responded, "With all due respect sir, we did it for the patient."

What is a Patient Advocate?

A co-worker recently told me that she could never do my job. I responded that yes, she could. I told her that the job *just* required someone with a compassionate, caring spirit. She said again that the job was too difficult and she couldn't believe I was still in this role after 13 years.

Having heard the same thing from other staff in the past, I stopped to reflect on the role of a patient advocate, and began to make a mental list of some of the things I dealt with *just that week.* ...

I had listened to many people in person and over the phone who were upset by circumstances; some of the hospital's making, others from family issues and some resulting from life events. I realized that I had interacted with dozens of good people just about these issues alone.

My heart still ached from the previous day for the young couple whose three-month old had stopped breathing. I watched in awe as this poor family experienced a tremendous loss and still managed to show incredible love and support for each grieving family member. I watched the emergency department staff wipes tears away after working nobly but fruitlessly to save this beautiful little life.

I dealt with the police as they investigated this death. It is difficult to put into words the emotions resulting from seeing a strapping police officer reduced to tears at the sight of this precious little one. I counted it a privilege to assist him by carefully holding the baby while he checked for signs of abuse or neglect – all a normal part of his role in this kind of tragedy.

Watching parents say goodbye to their child, leaves a lasting mark on your heart. Yet even in such terrible pain and anguish, these parents offered hugs and thanks for the tiny bit of comfort we could offer.

I remembered starting that day by dropping off a tube of poly-grip to our psych facility for a patient who thought it might help secure a tooth broken off a bridge.

I recalled taking clothes to a patient who needed something to wear at discharge. He thanked me for the clothes and asked if I could also get him a pair of steel-toed boots for work. The staff chuckled and quietly asked me if I could possibly find him a job, a place to live and a paycheck while I was at it. I squelched my overwhelming urge to say, "And would you like fries with that order?"

Back at the office I answered what seemed like a hundred phone calls, e- mails, pages and voice mail messages.

Then just when it seemed that I had nothing left to give, my office door flew open and in walked a man who looked exactly like Tiny Tim. I could not take my eyes off his dyed jet-black hair, wild clothes and the sun glasses plastered to *that* hair. He had questions about his hospital bill. For a moment I began to wonder *what had actually happened to Tiny Tim,* but I abruptly brought my mind back to the present and answered his questions.

I laughed over the comical things patients and families had said, such as "The doctor used his sketch-a-scope (that is, stethoscope) to listen to my heart." "I was diagnosed with indigo" (vertigo). "I need to see a gin-a-cologist." (We're pretty sure this person was looking for a gynecologist).

That week I had written letters to patients who had serious concerns about the quality of care they received.

I fretted about the many tasks and projects still to be completed, although experience had taught me that each would get done, one-by-one.

I then realized that I needed to correct my thinking; there are many compassionate and caring spirits in this world, but those traits are *not* enough to be a patient rep.

Being a patient rep takes a deep love for people, an optimistic view of life, and a belief that there are solutions to the troubling issues healthcare is faced with today. It takes a core belief that as an individual, I can and do make a difference for every person who has contact with me. It takes willingness to swim against the current and to stand up for what is right. It takes a desire to bring different and sometimes unpopular views to the table, and willingness to be the voice for patients who cannot speak for themselves. It takes the ability to laugh at ourselves and with others.

A patient rep must to have the ability to celebrate the small everyday miracles! What a true gift this is!

When a Grapefruit Is Not Just a Grapefruit

It was early on in my life as a patient advocate that I got a call from ICU. My role wasn't really understood by all the hospital staff at that point but basically when they weren't sure whom to call about something, they called us!

It seems there was a patient in ICU who was critically ill, and hadn't eaten anything in days. The family was sure that one of his last requests for a grapefruit would mean a great deal. Well, hospitals seldom offer grapefruit as it can interfere with many medications. The ICU staff called and asked me if I could "access" some grapefruit for this man.

The flexibility of the role of patient rep allowed me to leave the hospital, go to a nearby supermarket and procure a couple of grapefruit. I then proceeded to bring what I thought was a special dietary request to the patient's family. What happened next was an experience that really made me realize what a unique role we play in the hospital.

The patient's family was thrilled to be able to feed the patient his favorite comfort food. The patient who had been semi-conscious really seemed to perk up at the smell of the fruit being peeled.
He only ate a section or two at a time, but the family was so glad to be able to have had some ability to bring pleasure to the patients last few days. The staff felt good that they were able to see follow through on a patient request.

As I watched the family, I realized that one of our main functions as a patient advocate is to be a "catalyst" for interventions. It was only a grapefruit, but it had a tremendous amount of impact on this patient/family experience. I think that is true of a lot of what we as patient advocates do. I learned that day that most things have more meaning than face value.

Where Oh Where Has My Wedding Band Gone?

Henry is an interesting patient. He is in his 70's and has ALWAYS had his way. He has retired from his town Selectman position, but knows he still has plenty of clout. When he registers for a service, the nurses cringe hoping he isn't assigned to them.

Henry attended his Rotary meeting one noontime not long ago. He stood up, cleared his throat, and began to speak of his experience at our hospital a month ago. The hospital administrators began getting a bit edgy about exactly what Henry might say. Henry had nothing but praise. He spoke of our ED, day surgery, and medical/surgery units. He spoke of his surgeons and nurses, of the food and the accommodations.
Yes, Henry was pleased.

After the meeting, Henry approached our hospital CEO. He assured him that everything he said was true; HOWEVER, there was one small problem. Henry reported that upon arriving home, he realized that he no longer had his wedding ring. He said it was OK, but just in case a ring was found, he wanted us to know. Our CEO told Henry he would see what he could do.
When he arrived at the hospital, he called me and asked that I investigate.

I looked in the lost & found and called the floors, but no one had the ring. I decided to check Henry's medical record, no small feat given the size. On the common database page was a small notation from a day surgery nurse, "yellow ring in black bag".
What is a black bag? I had never heard of it!

I went to the day surgery nurse manager. She had never heard of a black bag, nor had her staff. She checked the staff sheet and found that Chuck, a tall, young, male nurse had been with Henry. She called Chuck over and I asked him if he knew. "Oh, of course I remember Henry. He was a great guy. Yeah, I took his wedding band, put it in a Ziploc bag, and told him I was putting it in the pocket of the black leather bag he had brought with him."

Our CEO called Henry, and lo and behold, there was the ring, right where Chuck said he had placed it a month ago. Henry now thinks we are THE BEST hospital around, and promises to relate the rest of the story to Rotary this week.

World War I Hero and His Sweetie

A 90-year-old patient came into my office because he was having a difficult time receiving a benefit he was entitled to. This man was a veteran of WWI. He was wounded and had to swim in the English Channel to save his life. Just his presence and his accomplishments deserve honor and respect.

Veterans who live more than 50 miles from a VA hospital may be entitled to receive travel reimbursement. This veteran was entitled to this benefit. This veteran came to his scheduled appointment, and after his appointment he proceeded to go to the travel office to collect his travel pay; only to find that the office did not have change and could not give him his travel pay at that time. The veteran was entitled to 60 cents. This was the amount that he would be given after Congress took out a mandatory deductible. This patient knew that he would receive 60 cents this day, and he expected 60 cents; however, the travel clerk did not have 60 cents in change to give him. Needless to say, the veteran came to my office.

He walked into my office and said, "Young man, I have a problem that I know you can fix. I am entitled to 60 cents in travel pay today and they tell me I cannot have it today because they have no change. I do not accept this." I talked to this veteran about his history in the military, his quest for a Purple Heart, and how he valued the VA Hospital.

Recognizing that this veteran lived through the depression era, I knew that 60 cents meant a lot to him. I asked him, "If I take 60 cents out of my pocket and give it to you right now, knowing that I can get the 60 cents back from our travel clerk, will you accept it". He said to me, "Yes, young man, I will accept the 60 cents, but you must retrieve your 60 cents from the travel clerk because it is the right thing to do." I reached into my pocket and pulled out 60 cents and I gave it to the man. He graciously thanked me and said, "It is people like you that truly care about people, and thank God that this hospital has you." I simply smiled and thanked him for his dedication to our country.

I noticed that the patient was not moving very well and I asked him how he got to the hospital today, and he looked at me and smiled and said "My sweetie, my wife, drove me today."

I asked where she was and he said to me with a huge smile on his face, "Well, you know, when you get to be our age you become rigid in your routines and this has certainly happened to my wife. She eats lunch every morning at 11, and just because I have to come to the doctor is no exception. She is in the cafeteria eating her lunch".

I could not help but smile and I asked him if he had money to buy lunch, and he said that he had a little money on him. I offered him four dollars worth of cafeteria coupons to get him some lunch, and then I offered him an additional one-dollar coupon and specifically said to him, "I want you to take this $1 coupon and when you go through the cafeteria line, I want you to buy your sweetie, your wife, an ice-cream". He smiled, thanked me and said, "She sure will be surprised". He left my office.

A bit later, I saw this veteran and his sweetie standing in my door smiling. She said to me, "I want to thank you for helping my husband. I was hungry, so I sent him to see you knowing you would help. I was very surprised when he sat down and handed me an ice cream and said that the young, nice, balding patient advocate said to give this to me. What a treat. Would you terribly mind if I kissed you on the cheek?" I said, "No, I would appreciate that. I can always use a kiss on the cheek".

It was so rewarding to witness how the job of a patient advocate benefits those whom it is intended to help.

You Don't Have to Have the Title to be a Patient Advocate

For reasons of patient safety, most hospitals have firm rules about children under six not being allowed in the nursery.
However, sometimes it becomes very clear that occasional exceptions are appropriate. This is one of those times.

Brian, only four years old, was very excited. He had a new baby brother. When Brian's grandparents went to Cindy, a relatively new nurse, to see if Brian could meet his new brother, Cindy took him to the nursery window. The grandparents then quickly explained to Cindy why Brian would have to "see" Kevin in a different way...because Brian was blind. After taking a few more minutes out of her busy schedule to listen, Cindy invited Brian into the nursery to meet his new brother. His beaming smile clearly showed how delighted Brian was to touch his brother's face.

Twenty-five years later, Cindy is still a nursery nurse. This experience changed her outlook as a nurse forever, and she credits this small child because of his very valuable gift early in her nursing career.

Made in the USA
San Bernardino, CA
07 May 2014